WITHDRAWAL

PHYSICAL CONDITIONING

The Barnes Dollar Sports Library

This library of practical sports books covers fundamentals, techniques, coaching and playing hints and equipment for each sport. Leading coaches and players have been selected to write these books, so each volume is authoritative and based upon actual experience. Photographs or drawings, or both, illustrate techniques, equipment and play.

ARCHERY
by Reichart & Keasey

BAIT CASTING
by Gilmer Robinson

BASEBALL
by Daniel E. Jessee

BASKETBALL
by Charles C. Murphy

BASKETBALL FOR GIRLS
by Meissner & Meyers

BETTER BADMINTON
by Jackson & Swan

BOWLING
by Falcaro & Goodman

BOXING
by Edwin L. Haislet

FENCING
by Joseph Vince

FIELD HOCKEY FOR GIRLS
by Josephine T. Lees

FLY CASTING
by Gilmer Robinson

FOOTBALL
by W. Glenn Killinger

GOLF
by Patty Berg

HANDBALL
by Bernath E. Phillips

HOW TO TIE FLIES
by E. C. Gregg

ICE HOCKEY
by Edward Jeremiah

JIU-JITSU
by Frederick P. Lowell

LACROSSE
by Tad Stanwick

PHYSICAL CONDITIONING
by Stafford & Duncan

RIDING
by J. J. Boniface

RIFLE MARKSMANSHIP
by Lt. Wm. L. Stephens

ROPING
by Bernard S. Mason

SIX-MAN FOOTBALL
by Ray O. Duncan

SKATING
by Putnam & Parkinson

SKIING
by Walter Prager

SOCCER AND SPEEDBALL
FOR GIRLS
by Florence L. Hupprich

SOFTBALL
by Arthur T. Noren

SWIMMING
by R. J. H. Kiphuth

TABLE TENNIS
by Jay Purves

TENNIS
by Helen Jacobs

TOUCH FOOTBALL
by John V. Grombach

TRACK AND FIELD
by Ray M. Conger

VOLLEY BALL
by Robert Laveaga

WRESTLING
by E. C. Gallagher

Clair Bee's Basketball Library

THE SCIENCE OF COACHING   MAN-TO-MAN DEFENSE AND ATTACK

ZONE DEFENSE AND ATTACK   DRILLS AND FUNDAMENTALS

A. S. BARNES AND COMPANY • *Publishers* • NEW YORK

Physical Conditioning

EXERCISES FOR SPORTS
AND HEALTHFUL LIVING

By

George T. Stafford

and

Ray O. Duncan

University of Illinois

ILLUSTRATED

A. S. BARNES AND COMPANY

New York

97

PRINTED IN THE UNITED STATES OF AMERICA

PREFACE

For some time prior to America's entrance into the war there was a strong feeling that World War II was a war of machines. Splendid regiments of trained men were ruthlessly swept aside or mercilessly trampled over by a mighty German war "machine." The superior German war "machine" made possible the early German victories. It was generally conceded that if the Allies were to stop the Germans they would have to build bigger and better machines than those used by the enemy. Some did not realize that the famed Panzer Divisions were noted for the vigor of the men as well as the speed and power of their machines.

The present munition race, with its emphasis on planes, tanks, guns, ships, and other implements of modern warfare, as well as the race to produce war materials such as oil, gasoline, steel, rubber, and other like materials, gives evidence of the fact that we are still considering this war as a war of machines.

With painful slowness and much confusion has come the newer move to consider the MANPOWER necessary to manipulate these machines and materials of war. Without attempting to minimize the great importance of machines and other equipment needed to win this war, there is the necessity for strong, courageous, skilful men to manipulate these machines.

While it is generally recognized that the men who will actually fight this war must be in the best possible condition, the "non-combatants" must also accept their responsibility to be in the best possible physical condition. The men at the various fronts must be supported by an army of workers behind the lines. Everyone must be fit for whatever his task may be.

The record of our athletes in the last war was an impressive one, and very few athletes were rejected because of physical defects. Athletics are ideal for promoting physical fitness—a very important phase of "Total Fitness." The physical fitness of every one of us must be improved.

This book is primarily intended for use by coaches in the

guidance of the potential athlete in order that he may reach his goal of perfection. The exercises recommended for conditioning are the activities used by many outstanding coaches. This book also aims to guide the non-athlete so that he can achieve his highest level of physical fitness. The athlete has a duty to perform in the perpetuation of this democracy; the worker behind the armed forces has his and her duty to perform in supporting our fighting men. Physical fitness makes the task of the fighter and the fighter's supporters much easier. It also makes living more enjoyable. Let us all aspire to reach the optimum of physical fitness.

Although many readers may not aspire to that degree of physical fitness which is demanded of the athlete, short series of exercises taken regularly are recommended for this group for the purpose of raising its level of physical fitness. Exercise series have been arranged to meet the needs of those who desire to keep themselves in better condition for their daily tasks.

G. T. S.
R. O. D.

CONTENTS

CHAPTER I

What is Meant by Physical Fitness?

The term physical fitness has become a common expression used to identify the movement which aims to bring back the virility and robustness which typified the men who built this great Nation of ours. These sturdy pioneers possessed a type of fitness characterized by the efficient functioning of all body parts as shown in their ability to adapt themselves to the environmental demands of their time.

The individual who is physically fit has a well-proportioned and a well-developed body, without a surplus of soft fat, and his posture is usually good. He has adequate muscular strength for his needs, and this strength is well controlled. He performs his activities with a high degree of motor proficiency. He has a supple, well-balanced body which he uses in a skilful, well-co-ordinated manner, and with a minimum of energy expended. The physically fit individual usually has an alert mind. He also has that confidence, courage, initiative, pride, and self-discipline which accompanies good morale. Finally, he has an abundance of energy which allows him to push himself to the limits of his endurance in sustained activities involving speed, power, and strength without ill effects. His body is functioning with a maximum of efficiency.

In addition to physical fitness one must also be socially and mentally fit to be able to adapt himself to the demands of his environment. This process of adaptation involves then the social and mental, as well as the physical phases of health. Physical fitness involves both the qualities of the man and his ideals. The picture of the man who is physically fit reveals unmistakable signs of confidence, courage, alertness, initiative, pride, discipline, and good posture.

There are many factors involved in promoting physical fitness. Our nutritional status must be improved. Approximately one-third of the people of the United States are improperly nourished. Many are overweight, and a greater number are underweight. The question of optimum, or ideal weight, cannot be determined by the tables found on the average penny weighing machine. A medical examination is the best procedure for determining a person's nutritional status as well as his health status in general.

Emotional stability, or the mental side of total fitness, is the least understood of all the ingredients of fitness. A person who is mentally fit feels that he is doing something which is worth while, and this effort brings recognition from his associates. He has a worth-while purpose in life, and he expends the greater part of his time achieving that purpose. The well-adjusted person realizes and practices the principle that regular diversion of thought and effort away from work sends him back to his work refreshed and ready to face his tasks with renewed vigor and enthusiasm. Emotional stability is needed in order that we may endure the many sacrifices which accompany and follow war.

The definition of physical fitness is not simple. However, if one keeps in mind the physical, social, and mental factors, he will view physical fitness as composed of qualities best represented by strength, power, speed, skill and endurance for the task, plus proper enthusiasm (mental equilibrium, morale, and mind-set) as shown in that feeling of responsibility for continued effort necessary for the completion of the task.

Our Present Health Status.

Our present health status is not so good as we should like it to be. The young men of our country are soft! We have been training our youth for the joys of living in a peaceful democracy. We do not have today the same type of rugged individuals who opened our prairies and conquered our wilderness. The men and women who pushed their way westward to the Pacific were strong, virile individuals. Up to a period shortly after the turn of the century, we had people with strong back muscles, stamina, and courage. Today, in too many cases, perhaps, we have only the courage. We are now reaping the benefits of our forefathers' enterprises in the form of steam heat, electricity, automobiles, air-conditioned houses, inner-spring mattresses, and other comforts of civilized living.

William Shirer in "Berlin Diary" compares the British and the German soldiers. He describes the British as hollow-chested, skinny, and round-shouldered—the products of years of office work. The Germans are described as clean-cut physically, healthy-looking as lions with well-developed chests—the products of years of hard disciplined exercise and training in the open air and sunshine. How would he describe many of our selectees—the products of years of training in a peaceful democracy?

For many years our Nation has enjoyed the countless inventions which have removed most of the toil from life. We lead the world in conveniences and labor-saving devices. While this has been very pleasant, these products of the machine age have caused a biological softening of our people which is incongruous with the picture of a nation at war against ruthless aggressors who are both physically fit and well-trained in the tactics of modern warfare. The majority of the people of the United States, except for a small group of trained athletes, lack the essential qualities of robustness, strength, physical and emotional stamina, endurance, and the general ability to use their bodies skilfully in *sustained effort* for a long period of time. They do not possess that standard of physical fitness which is characterized by strength, power, endurance, agility, stamina, and the other qualities of mankind so necessary for carrying out the activities of modern warfare.

In a recent study of a large number of male students at the University of Illinois, the School of Physical Education discovered the following facts:

13 per cent were unable to swim
36 per cent were able to swim, but less than 50 yards
 3 per cent were unable to chin themselves once
23 per cent were unable to chin five times
24 per cent were unable to jump over a hurdle waist high
41 per cent were unable to "skin the cat"
  Many could not run one-half mile at a slow jog without becoming completely exhausted.
  A large per cent of the students were round-shouldered, flabby, and clumsy.

A few years ago the answer to such a presentation of facts would have been, "So what?" Today, however, we are at war, and everyone realizes that our task is to gird ourselves for a struggle which, in addition to brains, demands strength, endurance, and courage to fight for our American way of life—to fight for survival.

In spite of the important part played by machines, man is still the essential ingredient of modern warfare. General Lear is credited with having said, "Man is the master machine in war. Equipment is not a substitute for character, spirit, dogged determination, dash, development of tactical skill, and the will to close with the enemy and destroy him."

Our immediate task is to make as many people as possible physically fit, whether it be for service in the armed forces, in the factories, on the farms, or in the ranks of professional service. The degree of physical fitness may vary for the different services, but the basic integral factors are the same. The men in the armed forces will have to endure more strenuous physical and mental demands than those in other services, but all of the people of our Nation must become physically fit for whatever services are demanded of them.

A Nation Fit for "Service." (The demands of war upon the people.)

A person who is to serve in the armed forces should know what will be demanded of him. The government makes this clear:

> To perform his duties satisfactorily, the soldier must possess great organic vigor, muscular and nervous strength, endurance, and agility. The average recruit does not possess the degree of physical fitness required of a trained soldier. The required degree of physical fitness can be acquired only through physical training. The performance of purely military exercises, that is, drill, marching, etc., is not alone sufficient to correct the deficiencies and incorrect postures too often acquired before becoming a soldier. Further, the complexities of modern warfare require so much technical training for the soldier that all too frequently no time is allotted for physical training; yet the soldier who possesses great technical skill but is unable to withstand the rigorous life demanded is of questionable value.[1]

Democracy has long protected the rights of individuals and the sacredness of personality. It is now the duty of each individual in turn to protect and perpetuate that order which has been placed under desperate attack and siege by totalitarianism. No one can avoid his part in this task, nor retire from his responsibility of American citizenship.

This Nation has passed through an era of soft living and rampant individualism. Today as a result, there is a tremendous effort being made in all the armed forces of the Nation to correct the result of this long period of wasteful existence. The rejection figures for physical defects released by the Selective Service Commission are staggering. The armed forces are succeeding slowly with the actual training and the mental and the physical conditioning of their men. While this is being done, *other young men of the Nation should be taking time by*

[1] Basic Field Manual. *Physical Training*. Washington: Government Printing Office, 1941, p. 1.

the forelock so that the job will be less weighty for the armed forces when they join the ranks.[2]

War exerts a tremendous drain on all our resources. War is not pleasant to contemplate or to endure. It means sacrifices. It means marching with heavy packs over rough ground, digging trenches, climbing in and out of these trenches, and running up and down steep hills. At times, it is necessary to crawl over the ground on one's belly. This war, as has been the case with all other wars, will be conducted out of doors and in all sorts of weather. There will be the necessity for swimming fully clothed in icy water, jumping or climbing over obstacles, etc. All these activities are quite different from the normal activities of peace time. These activities require physical stamina, faultless mental health, proper evaluation of propaganda, and resourceful thinking. One must have something more than courage and good morale to win this war. Man, the master machine, must be able to expend large amounts of physical effort. The capacity for efficient performance of these wartime activities is necessary if one is to survive this struggle.

There is a cock-sureness about the American people which is very valuable and, at the same time, dangerous. We must realize that strength, power, endurance, agility, stamina, and skill are necessary in a high degree to supplement the indomitable courage and morale which we believe to be our heritage. But we must not overlook the fact that our enemies possess these physical qualities and an emotional fervor which compares favorably with ours. Courage alone was not sufficient to defend Wake Island as it was defended. The loyal defenders of Wake were trained, well-disciplined soldiers. Our enemies are fighting for their very existence. We must possess that hardier, sturdier personnel which will deal the final blow for victory and a lasting peace.

While the demands of modern warfare are great, there is no reason to believe that we cannot overcome our present weaknesses. The condition is not one of real weakness, but rather lethargy. Conditioning is necessary to strengthen our moral and muscle fibers, overcome our internal weaknesses, and make us ready to endure. We have the brains. We know what our task is. If we use our brains we can survive, even in a world where some of the people have developed a national spirit whose objective seems to be the ruthless

[2] Letter from Navy Rear Admiral to University Presidents, 1942.

destruction of all other races. Our immediate task is to raise our physical fitness level. In addition to improving our nutritional status, the correction of physical defects by the doctor and the dentist, there is the need for conditioning our bodies through exercise.

Many athletes break training as soon as the season ends. Their daily way of living is not conducive to maintaining a high degree of physical fitness. Consequently, it is necessary for them to regain adequate physical condition before resuming their sport. The conditioning activities suggested for the various sports are those used by many outstanding coaches. These exercises have been successfully used for many years.

The athlete reaches his high degree of fitness through the aid of various factors such as good heredity and practicing the accepted health habits—one of which is engaging regularly in big-muscle physical activity. Too many men and women have neglected the exercise phase of health habits. True, they do not need to engage so extensively in vigorous activities as does the athlete. But, no exercise at all is undesirable. For the purpose of getting in shape and maintaining a higher standard of physical fitness, exercise is a necessity. This does not mean reading about or watching sports, but actually *performing* sports suitable to one's age and physical capacity.

The exercises for the non-athlete have been arranged to take care of those who can give only a small amount of time daily to this important health habit. Exercises particularly suitable for women have also been included in this manual.

CHAPTER II

We Must Work to be Fit.

For years too many of us Americans have neglected to engage in regular, systematic exercise. Our life in a peaceful democracy has been pleasant, and our main objective has been to enjoy life. Hedonism must be replaced by a work-duty philosophy. Few people, except the young men training for varsity teams and the professional athletes preparing for a sport, have made a determined effort to reach and maintain a top physical condition. Many are satisfied to be "tolerably well." One of our greatest obstacles to physical fitness has been our desire to secure health with a minimum of effort. We are too prone to seek "short cuts" to health. We read advertisements of "one-shot health vitamins" and think that we have found the panacea for our self-diagnosed ills. We go on freak diets and too frequently do not consult a physician until all else has failed.

America is known as the land of sports; however, there has not been a widespread, intensive participation in vigorous sports. A visit to any of our large bathing beaches during the summer will reveal thousands of individuals clad in bathing suits and lying on the sand. Less than 10 per cent of this group actually swim more than ten yards at a time. Some don't even swim! Too many prefer the lighter, less vigorous sports. Cross country running is considered too strenuous for many high school boys.

The war has focused attention upon physical fitness. Examination of selectees for military service has shown a high percentage of defective young men. Today, a large number of our people are really interested in means of improving physical fitness. How should one best proceed to raise his physical fitness status?

Before one engages in a program of exercise, it is essential that he have a careful medical examination to determine his present health status. No program of exercise should be attempted without this important prerequisite. In many instances poor physical condition

7

is due to some defect which can be corrected only by medical treatment. If the medical examination reveals no organic or other body disturbances which would make it unwise to engage in exercise, the individual is ready to improve his physical fitness through exercise.

Physical fitness is highly specific. A person may be fit for one sport, yet he may perform very poorly in another. A swimmer may be poorly conditioned for wrestling. However, certain features of physical fitness remain constant. Everyone today needs to be physically fit for whatever task he has to perform. All of our men of military age should be physically fit for military service. The athlete needs to be in excellent physical condition if he expects to perform well in his sport. Emphasis needs to be put upon vigorous activities such as jumping, running, climbing, swimming, weight lifting, etc. Combative sports such as boxing, wrestling, and football are highly recommended for the development of a war-time physical fitness.

It is impossible for everyone to develop physical fitness through participation in vigorous, rugged sports. However, everyone can engage in conditioning exercises to raise his physical fitness level.

Good physical condition has many advantages for everyone. The conditioning exercises given in this book can be used for the purpose of simply getting into condition. It is our patriotic duty to be in the best possible condition in order to work more efficiently. However, it does not prove satisfactory for the majority of people to confine their conditioning program to calisthenic exercises alone. Calisthenic exercises are intended to put a person in condition to participate in and enjoy sports. Sports are inherently interesting, but it is necessary to be in condition in order to perform well and thoroughly enjoy sports activities.

Too many people function below their normal capacity. We must learn to increase the demands on the body and develop greater power, strength, and endurance for sustained effort. Progressive demands must be made on our bodies. We must work for poise and skill in the use of our bodies.

Benefits of Exercise.

Exercise benefits the individual in many ways. The physical benefits should be improved posture, flexibility, agility, good balance, increased strength, power, and endurance. The functions of the various systems of the body are improved by exercise. The general circulation of the body is accelerated which results in food and oxygen being carried more efficiently to the body tissues. The excretory system functions better, and the elimination of body waste is facilitated. Digestion is aided by exercise and, if the body is supplied with an adequate diet, better assimilation of nourishment results. Repeated doses of exercise stimulate body growth; strength, power, and endurance result.

In addition to physical development, exercise has a soothing effect upon the nervous system. During exercise the nervous system becomes more active but with less resulting fatigue than during sedentary mental work. The physical fatigue which comes from vigorous exercise serves as a mental tonic. There is a great mental or emotional satisfaction which accompanies a high degree of physical fitness. A person who is physically fit does not have to apologize for being unable to engage in an activity. He finds himself able to do many things formerly considered beyond his capacity. When the desire for activity has been satisfied through the performance of wholesome physical activities, significant mental satisfactions follow. One feels a certain pride in his accomplishment, and he secures group recognition and social approval. This feeling of self-sufficiency develops better morale. The simple ability to chin one's self ten times causes many individuals to hold up their chest with pride and satisfaction. The person who is physically fit has an indescribable feeling within him of virility and power. He is much better prepared for meeting the problems of his day than if he were "soft" and out of condition.

Exercise should be considered at this time as a very important means of remedying the past neglect of the body from the organic side. Although the body has not been given sufficient exercise, Nature quickly helps to remedy this past neglect. A program of exercise, which involves the large muscles of the body and which is not too severe at the start, soon finds the body responding to this activity. The organic systems begin to show new energy. The muscular system begins to become better toned, and the flesh becomes more firm. There is a liveliness and responsiveness and a new energy which are suitable rewards for the aching muscles that follow the first day of exercising. Gradually the body shows greater endurance and more capacity for work, and there is a rapid recovery from fatigue. Finally, some semblance of skill is manifested. All of this is very satisfying.

CHAPTER III

Have a Health Examination Today!

While it cannot be denied that the process of increasing one's physical strength, endurance, power, etc., is largely dependent upon physical exercise, certain prerequisites must be satisfied before starting the exercise program. A careful medical and dental examination should be taken as the initial step in the process of increasing one's physical fitness. Are YOU in condition to exercise? Infection in the system, a weak heart, or any of the other frequent bodily disturbances must be ruled out before attempting the exercise program. This applies to the athlete as well as to the non-athlete. No sports conditioning program should be undertaken before having had a health examination. See your doctor today!

Since many people are improperly nourished, this condition must be treated before one can hope to secure the beneficial effects of exercise. A well-balanced diet is needed to supply the body with the energy which this increased exercise program demands. In addition to the exercise program, one should practice regularly the accepted health habits. Sufficient sleep, rest, and relaxation are important.

Conditioning for Sports.

Sports occupy an important place in the American way of life. They are recognized as an integral part of our school program. Now that we are at war, greater emphasis is being placed upon physical fitness, and more recognition is being given to the value of our sports program. The value of sports is very aptly stated in the follow quotation from the Chicago Sun of March 22, 1942:

> The best soldier is the athlete, his muscles attuned to the rigors of competition, his mind alert to strategic calculation of the opposition's weaknesses, his whole being inoculated with the burning desire to WIN!

A number of coaches with long experience believe that too little emphasis is placed upon conditioning in sports today. Too many youngsters are out of condition due to soft living more often than they are in condition due to vigorous daily activities. These coaches argue that too much time is given to the development of skills with a subsequent neglect of physical development. However, all coaches agree that an athlete must be in good physical condition to play well in any sport. The differences in opinion arise as to the amount of time which should be spent on conditioning and the method to be used to obtain the desired results. The committee on the contribution of College Physical Education to National Preparedness made the following statement in its report of April 23, 1942:

> We must continue with our programs of swimming, golf, tennis, baseball, football, soccer, running, handball, squash, fencing, basketball, and other sports, including in the training of men for each sport *those conditioning exercises* so essential to efficient performance as used by our *most intelligent teachers and coaches.*

In recent years the idea has spread in our sports world that you learn to do anything whatsoever by *doing it.* This is a reaction against drills of one sort or another in lieu of actual practice of sports under game conditions, or actual performance of some event or sport, such as learning a swimming stroke on a piano bench, instead of in the water. There is no doubt that the best way to learn a game is to play it; the best way to learn football, basketball, golf, or swimming is to play football, basketball, golf, or to swim. This reaction has probably led away from proper conditioning for games and sports and has done away with worth-while drills and exercises which would not only fit one to do well in a sport, but would also contribute to the development of skills essential to it.

Track coaches early discovered that running five or six miles would not fit the athlete to run the mile race, rather it would fit him to run five or six miles. Following this came the idea in track of the over-distance for speed and pace. For example, the over-distance for the 440 yard run generally used was 600 yards, and the under-distance was 300. Then one of our foremost track coaches conceived the notion that the closer the over and under-distances were to the actual length of the race, the better it would prepare the athlete for that distance. Returning to the 440 yard race as an example, the suggested under-distance is 350 yards, and the over-distance is 500 yards. This seems like a sound idea for sports. In the pre-season practice the sessions may be of any length, within reason, that may be necessary to establish the skills and team play requisite to the game. During the competitive season, however, the practice sessions could well follow the over and under-distance idea of track. That is, the practice sessions should last a little under or a little over the time the activity will require and accomplish about the same amount of work at the same speed.

Keep this thought in mind. If you practice football or basketball twice as long as a game lasts, you are probably conditioning your players to distribute their energy over a distance which is too long and not geared to game conditions. This applies to the actual season and not necessarily to pre-season practice.

The conditioning exercises given in Chapter V are ideal for developing physical fitness for all sports as well as for military training and for civilian work of all kinds. All of them are excellent for keeping the athlete in condition during off-season so that when the season starts he is ready to go. At a coaching clinic a number of years ago someone asked Glenn Cunningham when he started to get in condition for track. The great miler replied that he was never out of condition. The track season to him simply meant more running and a lot of work on form, pace, etc. That is the picture of an ideal athlete. Anyone who strives for excellence in athletic performance should never let himself get out of condition. But, unfortunately, too many do! A summer spent as lifeguard at one of the many beaches does not condition the individual to play football. He needs conditioning before he is ready to endure the rigors of football.

Coaches of the various sports differ in their selection of conditioning exercises for use during the actual sport season. The skills required by various sports require different types of physical conditioning. It is essential that the exercises be closely related to the skill demanded by the particular sport. Running is an ideal example of a conditioning activity for football.

Chapter IV deals with the conditioning procedures for the common sports.

Conditioning for the Non-athlete.

Primitive man had little choice in the matter of exercise. If he wished to survive he had to engage in many forms of activity. Today, one must plan to allow time for healthful exercise. He must find a place where he can exercise. Exercise should be adapted to the individual's age and present physical condition. Those who have done little or no systematic exercising must naturally go easy at first. As much as three weeks may be needed before one can really start to engage in the more vigorous exercises. The series of exercises given in Chapter V have been selected to meet the needs of those who wish to achieve a high degree of physical fitness. Naturally, those who are not in good physical condition must not attempt to do all of these exercises the maximum number of times until the body has been slowly conditioned to this strain.

As an individual grows older his muscles and his arteries lose some of their elasticity. Arteries become thickened and are unable to withstand the strain of sudden or prolonged vigorous activity. Those under twenty-five years of age should be able to perform the majority of these exercises if they gradually increase the number of times each exercise is performed, and if they do these exercises *regularly*. Regularity is of very great importance. Irregular exercising may be actually dangerous.

A person should adapt his conditioning program to his physical condition as determined by a medical examination, and to his age. All of the exercises given in Chapter V are not recommended for all people. The more vigorous exercises such as "The Jeep" should only be taken by those under twenty-five years of age. The desk worker thirty years of age with little or no athletic experience while in school or college should avoid the more vigorous exercises and should be satisfied to perform the less vigorous activities the minimum number of times.

In all cases it is essential to use good judgment in selecting and performing calisthenic exercises. The best rule is to begin very slowly. Be satisfied to increase gradually the dosage of exercise. Five or ten years without exercising necessitates a reasonable length of time for recovery. For the busy person who can only give five minutes a day for the first few weeks it might be well to select an exercise for each of the body parts such as: No. 1, for posture and abdomen; No. 2, for strengthening the abdomen; No. 6 (first stage only), for arms, shoulders and legs; and No. 13, for raising the chest and strengthening the muscles of the upper back. (See Chapter V for details of these exercises.)

Remember your age! Men under thirty may exercise with more speed and span than those over thirty. After thirty, one should work for endurance and not for speed.

What Time of Day is Best for Exercising?

The athlete should take his conditioning exercises before his regular practice session or as a part of the practice session.

For the non-athlete, before breakfast is NOT the ideal time. The body is really not awake at this time. (Metabolism is low.) Exercising before breakfast is like racing a cold motor. Ten o'clock in the morning finds the body very much awake; the vital organs are functioning very efficiently, and fatigue has not started to become pronounced as yet. This hour is a very desirable time for exercising, if you can spare the time and if there is no "let down" or marked fatigue following exercising at this hour. Many people find this hour undesirable because it leaves them "tired" throughout the remainder of the day.

The ideal time for exercising is about three or four o'clock in the afternoon. The major portion of the day's work is over, and exercise helps to remove many of the waste products which have resulted from the day's work. Exercise at this time stimulates the body processes, opens the pores of the skin, and sharpens the appetite. One should find himself very refreshed following his exercise and bath. Four o'clock in the afternoon is the ideal time for the exercise period. Of course, for those who cannot leave their work until five o'clock this later hour has its advantages. The work of the day is over and the exercise should leave one refreshed and ready for whatever the evening may bring forth.

Having passed your health examination, you are now ready to exercise. Start now and exercise regularly. Self-discipline may be necessary in some instances, but the feeling of well-being after a few days exercising will more than repay you for the effort expended. Be satisfied to work slowly at first. Remember, if you have not been exercising for years, you cannot expect the body to spring back into good condition in a few days.

For the Ladies!

A special section of Chapter V is devoted to exercises for women.

CHAPTER IV

SPORTS CONDITIONING

A number of the more common sports are dealt with in this chapter and specific exercises are recommended for each sport. In addition, conditioning tips are given as well as additional exercises which have been found very beneficial by successful coaches for their particular sports.

Physical Fitness Fundamentals.

There are six fundamental qualities which are essential to develop basic fitness for sports. These are strength, power, endurance, flexibility, agility, and balance. The exercises recommended in this chapter give training in these six qualities. In addition to these physical characteristics there is that indefinable "X" quality which all great athletes have, but which cannot be developed by exercise. It has many names, such as mental stance, "heart," determination to win, intestinal fortitude, etc. This quality makes the great athlete "deliver in the pinch." The great athlete usually possesses all six of the fundamental qualities plus the "X" quality to play his best when the going is the hardest. In this chapter the various sports have been analyzed to select the fundamental physical qualities essential to skill in the sports, and exercises have been selected to develop these necessary qualities.

Time Schedule.

The average athlete would perform more effectively if he gave reasonable time to his conditioning activities. The following schedule of the amount of time spent on conditioning has received the approval of the majority of coaches:

First week .... 15 minutes
Second week .... 10 minutes
Third week .... 5 minutes
Fourth week and after .... Depending upon
condition of squad

Warm-up Series.

There is one thing common to all sports, and that is the importance of an athlete being properly "warmed up" before participation. The following set of warm-up exercises is recommended. They must be varied, of course, to meet any demand, but the "warm-up" principle remains the same.

Stationary jogging .... 2 minutes

Arm flinging—forward, up, back and down............ 10 times

Trunk twisting (all twisting above waist—keep hips firm)—feet apart, arms side shoulder level, twist right, front, left.
Twist left, front right .... 10 times

Squatting (half squat with arms thrust forward)........ 10 times

Side bending—feet apart, arms above head, bend right,
up, bend left, up .... 10 times

The body should show a slight perspiration at the end of this short warm-up series.

Organizing the Conditioning Drill.

For all team sports it is desirable to have the squad report at a given time so that drill can be given to all members. In individual sports a definite prescription of activities can be outlined to meet individual needs. In general, however, best results will be secured when the squad meets as a group and goes through the conditioning drill together.

1. Put plenty of pep into each exercise.
2. Use sport terminology wherever possible.
3. Keep up an intermittent chatter of encouragement.
4. Repeat each exercise only a few times at first to avoid undue fatigue.
5. Change from one exercise to another without any pause.
6. Name exercises after team members ("Smith Special," etc.). These may be given to the squad by the men for whom the exercises have been named.
7. Keep the whole thing moving fast.
8. Remember, in addition to muscular strength, emphasis must be given to timing and rhythm. Skilful movements must be the goal.

BASEBALL

A good baseball player must have strength and power in the arms, legs, wrists, and shoulders, yet it is essential that he not be muscular to the point of tightness. Flexibility, power, speed, and quick reaction are the essential qualities of a good baseball player. It is extremely important that a player have flexibility.

During the winter months, activities such as wood-chopping are good for the wrists, arms, and shoulders. A lot of snappy walking and some running are recommended for leg conditioning.

The conditioning program suggested for the first three weeks is as follows:

Roll and Sit Through

This exercise tests your abdominal muscles. It also develops flexibility, agility, and skill in the use of your body. If you find difficulty in "sitting through" (movement number 6), you may solve this difficulty by reducing the size of *your abdomen*.

Starting position:

Lying on back with arms above head on the floor and legs straight.

Exercise:

1. Bring knees to chest, grasp hard with hands. Exhale.
2. Stretch legs straight, heels six inches off floor, hands above head in line with the body (not touching floor).
3. Roll either right or left keeping feet and hands free from floor.
4. Place hands on floor under chest.
5. Extend arms raising weight on hands and feet.

6. Sit through, bending knees sharply and sliding feet forward *between* hands. Exhale.
7. Assume starting position and repeat.

Dosage: 4-10 times.

BOTTOMS UP

This exercise stretches the hamstrings (tendons at the back surface of the knee joint). Loss of flexibility of tendons is a sign of "getting old!" Here is one way to stay young.

Starting position:
Squat position, fingers grasping toes.

Exercise:
1. Straighten knees, keeping feet flat on floor and maintaining grasp of toes. Exhale.
2. Return to starting position.
3. Repeat.

Dosage: 10-20 times.

SINGLE TREADMILL

This exercise is a mild endurance exercise plus flexibility.

Starting position:
One-half dip position with right knee bent under chest, left leg extended back full length.

Exercise:
Rapidly change positions of feet by jumping motions.

Dosage: 30 seconds or 15-30 changes.

THE RUSSIAN

This exercise is a vigorous endurance exercise for the legs. Flexibility, agility, and balance are developed—but gradually. Avoid if you have a "trick" or weak knee.

Starting position:
Full squat, right leg straight forward with heel on floor.

Exercise:
1. Change leg position, placing left leg forward and right foot under body in full squat position. Exhale.
2. Repeat.

Dosage: 10-30 seconds or 6-20 changes.

JACK KNIFE

This exercise is a vigorous abdominal exercise and involves a high degree of balance, flexibility, and agility.

Starting position:
Lying on back, hands at sides.

Exercise:
1. Raise trunk and legs off floor keeping knees straight.
2. Touch toes with fingers. Exhale.
3. Return to starting position.
4. Repeat.

Dosage: 5-20 times.

Conditioning tips:
During the baseball season it is essential to warm up thoroughly before every practice. It is important to loosen all the muscles before

vigorous work is begun—especially the throwing muscles. Twisting, stretching, and bending are the actions to emphasize.

Tie up every exercise with a baseball skill. The exercise "Bottoms Up" is recommended for promoting flexibility of the hamstring tendons.

Have nothing contrary to flexibility.

Have pitchers hit "fungoes" to outfield as a stretching exercise.

Some coaches recommend that pitchers be careful not to sleep lying on their pitching arm the night before they are to pitch.

"Pepper drills" are good for conditioning and quick reaction.

Running cannot be stressed too much as a very important baseball conditioning activity. Jogging around the field can be used to develop wind and legs, and sprinting short distances develops baserunning ability.

BASKETBALL

Basketball demands flexibility, agility, endurance, and balance. Speed is essential, but it is quickness not "long" speed that is important. Jumping and stretching are predominant activities in basketball. A player who is tired loses flexibility, balance, and quickness; consequently, it is important to develop the endurance necessary to play a full game at top speed. In order to prepare a team for tournament play one must develop greater endurance because of the limited time for recuperation.

The conditioning program, not to exceed three weeks, is as follows:

ROLL AND SIT THROUGH

This exercise tests your abdominal muscles. It also develops flexibility, agility, and skill in the use of your body. If you find difficulty in "sitting through" (movement number 6), you may solve this difficulty by reducing the size of your abdomen.

Starting position:

Lying on back with arms above head on the floor and legs straight.

Exercise:

1. Bring knees to chest, grasp hard with hands. Exhale.
2. Stretch legs straight, heels six inches off floor, hands above head in line with the body (not touching floor).
3. Roll either right or left keeping feet and hands free from floor.
4. Place hands on floor under chest.
5. Extend arms raising weight on hands and feet.
6. Sit through, bending knees sharply and sliding feet forward *between* hands. Exhale.
7. Assume starting position and repeat.

Dosage: 4-10 times.

Bottoms Up

This exercise stretches the hamstrings (tendons at the back surface of the knee joint). Loss of flexibility of tendons is a sign of "getting old!" Here is one way to stay young.

Starting position:

Squat position, fingers grasping toes.

Exercise:

1. Straighten knees, keeping feet flat on floor and maintaining grasp of toes. Exhale.
2. Returning to starting position.
3. Repeat.

Dosage: 10-20 times.

SINGLE TREADMILL

This exercise is a mild endurance exercise plus flexibility.

Starting position:
One-half dip position with right knee bent under chest, left leg extended back full length.

Exercise:
Rapidly change positions of feet by jumping motions.

Dosage: 30 seconds or 15-30 changes.

THE RUSSIAN

This exercise is a vigorous endurance exercise for the legs. Flexibility, agility, and balance are developed—but gradually. Avoid if you have a "trick" or weak knee.

Starting position:
Full squat, right leg straight forward with heel on floor.

Exercise:
1. Change leg position, placing left leg forward and right foot under body in full squat position. Exhale.
2. Repeat.

Dosage: 10-30 seconds or 6-20 changes.

JACK KNIFE

This exercise is a vigorous abdominal exercise and involves a high degree of balance, flexibility, and agility.

Starting position:

Lying on back, hands at sides.

Exercise:

1. Raise trunk and legs off floor keeping knees straight.
2. Touch toes with fingers. Exhale.
3. Return to starting position.
4. Repeat.

Dosage: 5-20 times.

THE PINCER MOVEMENT

This exercise uses practically all the muscles of the body. For endurance, co-ordination, and flexibility. Especially recommended for strengthening abdominal muscles.

Starting position:

Lying on back, arms at side shoulder level.

Exercise:

1. Kick right foot to left hand and return. Exhale.
2. Kick left foot to right hand and return. Exhale.

3. Sit up, with legs spread wide apart. Exhale.
4. Swing right hand to left foot. Exhale.
5. Swing left hand to right foot. Exhale.
6. Roll to original position.
7. Repeat.

Dosage: 4-10 times.

The "V"

Victory over weak abdominal muscles!

This exercise looks simple. Vigorous exercise of the abdominal and leg muscles. It also helps to improve balance.

Starting position:

Lying on back, hands on abdomen which is pulled in.

Exercise:

1. Raise legs six inches, throwing body in a sitting position as legs are spread wide apart, *heels off floor.*
2. Close legs. Exhale.
3. Lower trunk to lying position and lower heels to floor.
4. Repeat.

Dosage: 4-12 times.

Hit the Deck

This exercise tests your endurance. The dive to the floor demands good hand, wrist, and arm strength and skill in the control of the body—and courage.

Starting position:

High-step run in place for 10 seconds.

Exercise:

1. Dive forward, weight on hands and let first the chest touch the floor *lightly,* then the abdomen, then the thighs, and feet. (Be sure to point toes.) Relax for 5 seconds.
2. Jump to feet.
3. Repeat.

Dosage: 4-10 times.

JUMPING JACK

This exercise strengthens the muscles of the thighs, calves, and feet. This is a fine test of endurance.

Starting position:

Standing, feet apart, arms over head.

Exercise:

1. Jump to squat, hands on hips. Exhale.
2. Spring back to original position. Inhale.
3. Repeat.

Dosage: 30 seconds to one minute.

DOUBLE TREADMILL

This exercise is a vigorous endurance exercise which gradually involves the hip and thigh muscles.

Starting position:
One-half dip position with both legs extended back full length.

Exercise:

1. Bring both knees up under chest with a jumping motion. Exhale.
2. Return feet to starting position with a jumping motion. Rapidly.

Dosage: 15-30 seconds.

THE JEEP

This exercise is a powerful strength, endurance, agility, and flexibility exercise as well as an excellent developer of the muscles of the legs.

Note: Do not start using this exercise until the second week of exercising.

Starting position:
Full squat position.

Exercise:

1. Jump high into the air spreading legs outward and upward keeping knees straight, touching toes to hands.
2. Let gravity take you to the starting position.
3. Repeat.

Dosage: 2-10 times.

Conditioning tips:
Basketball players should do a lot of running before the basketball season. Track and cross-country are good activities to develop legs and endurance.

Rope skipping is a good exercise to help a boy who has trouble being "on his toes."

A good early season drill which combines leg conditioning with footwork for defensive skill is the following: Line up the squad and have each player assume proper defense stance. At the command "left," "right," "back," "forward" the players move quickly in the direction commanded. These commands should be mixed and given quickly.

Basketball coaches should guard against "over-coaching." Due to the fact that the season is long and practice is never drudgery, it is easy to "over-coach" or "over-train" a team. After a team is in good physical condition and the season is under way, it is wise to reduce practice sessions to slightly over the length of time used in a game.

BOXING

Endurance, agility, strength, power, and balance are essential to the boxer. The arms, shoulders, legs, back, neck, and abdominal muscles must be strong.

The following exercises are recommended for the boxer for a period not to exceed three weeks:

Sit Ups

This exercise is excellent for strengthening the abdominal muscles. Try to pull abdomen well in throughout the exercise.

Starting position:

Lying on back with arms above head on the floor.

Exercise:

1. Sit up and touch toes. Keep legs straight. Exhale.
2. Roll back to floor, extending arms in line with body.
3. Repeat.

Dosage: 10-20 times.

Note: After two weeks do the "Sit Ups" as follows:

1. Clasp the hands behind the neck in the lying position.
2. Sit up and touch right elbow to left knee. Exhale.
3. Roll back to floor.
4. Sit up and touch left elbow to right knee. Exhale.
5. Roll back to floor.
6. Repeat.

Roll and Sit Through

This exercise tests your abdominal muscles. It also develops flexibility, agility, and skill in the use of your body. If you find difficulty in "sitting through" (movement number 6), you may solve this difficulty by reducing the size of your abdomen.

Starting position:
Lying on back with arms above head on the floor and legs straight.

Exercise:
1. Bring knees to chest, grasp hard with hands. Exhale.
2. Stretch legs straight, heels six inches off floor, hands above head in line with the body (not touching floor).
3. Roll either right or left keeping feet and hands free from floor.
4. Place hands on floor under chest.
5. Extend arms raising weight on hands and feet.
6. Sit through, bending knees sharply and sliding feet forward *between* hands. Exhale.
7. Assume starting position and repeat.

Dosage: 4-10 times.

JUMPING JACK

This exercise strengthens the muscles of the thighs, calves, and feet. This is a fine test of endurance.

Starting position:
Standing, feet apart, arms over head.

Exercise:
1. Jump to squat hands on hips. Exhale.
2. Spring back to original position. Inhale.
3. Repeat.

Dosage: 30 seconds to one minute.

The Pincer Movement

This exercise uses practically all the muscles of the body. For endurance, co-ordination, and flexibility. Especially recommended for strengthening abdominal muscles.

Starting position:

Lying on back, arms at side shoulder level.

Exercise:

1. Kick right foot to left hand and return. Exhale.
2. Kick left foot to right hand and return. Exhale.
3. Sit up, with legs spread wide apart. Exhale.
4. Swing right hand to left foot. Exhale.
5. Swing left hand to right foot. Exhale.
6. Roll to original position.
7. Repeat.

Dosage: 4-10 times.

The "V"

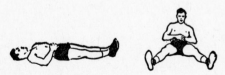

Victory over weak abdominal muscles! This exercise looks simple. Vigorous exercise of the abdominal and leg muscles. It also helps to improve balance.

Starting position:

Lying on back, hands on abdomen which is pulled in.

Exercise:

1. Raise legs six inches, throwing body in a sitting position as legs are spread wide apart, *heels off floor.*
2. Close legs. Exhale.
3. Lower trunk to lying position and lower heels to floor.
4. Repeat.

Dosage: 4-12 times.

HIT THE DECK

This exercise tests your endurance. The dive to the floor demands good hand, wrist, and arm strength and skill in the control of the body—and courage.

Starting position:

High-step run in place for 10 seconds.

Exercise:

1. Dive forward, weight on hands and let first the chest touch the floor *lightly,* then the abdomen, then the thighs, and feet. (Be sure to point toes.) Relax for 5 seconds.
2. Jump to feet.
3. Repeat.

Dosage: 4-10 times.

BOTTOMS UP

This exercise stretches the hamstrings (tendons at the back surface of the knee joint). Loss of flexibility of tendons is a sign of "getting old!" Here is one way to stay young.

Starting position:

Squat position, fingers grasping toes.

Exercise:

1. Straighten knees, keeping feet flat on floor and maintaining grasp of toes. Exhale.
2. Return to starting position.
3. Repeat.

Dosage: 10-20 times.

LEG LIFTER

This exercise stretches the muscles of the lower back and strengthens the muscles of the abdomen.

Starting position:

Lying on back, hands under head and elbows on floor.

Exercise:

1. With knees together and straight, extend legs upward to right angle to floor.
2. Keep elbows on floor, press heels toward ceiling six inches. (Legs are extended *up*.)
3. Return heels to a position six inches off floor.
4. Repeat.

Dosage: 4-16 times.

SINGLE TREADMILL

This exercise is a mild endurance exercise plus flexibility.

Starting position:
One-half dip position with right knee bent under chest, left leg extended back full length.

Exercise:
Rapidly change positions of feet by jumping motions.

Dosage: 30 seconds or 15-30 changes.

DOUBLE TREADMILL

This exercise is a vigorous endurance exercise which gradually involves the hip and thigh muscles.

Starting position:
One-half dip position with both legs extended back full length.

Exercise:
1. Bring both knees up under chest with a jumping motion. Exhale.
2. Return feet to starting position with a jumping motion. Rapidly.

Dosage: 15-30 seconds.

THE RUSSIAN

This exercise is a vigorous endurance exercise for the legs. Flexibility, agility, and balance are developed—but gradually. Avoid if you have a "trick" or weak knee.

Starting position:
Full squat, right leg straight forward with heel on floor.

Exercise:
1. Change leg position, placing left leg forward and right foot under body in full squat position. Exhale.
2. Repeat.

Dosage: 10-30 seconds or 6-20 changes.

JACK KNIFE

This exercise is a vigorous abdominal exercise and involves a high degre of balance, flexibility, and agility.

Starting position:
Lying on back, hands at sides.

Exercise:
1. Raise trunk and legs off floor keeping knees straight.
2. Touch toes with fingers. Exhale.
3. Return to starting position.
4. Repeat.

Dosage: 5-20 times.

THE JEEP

This exercise is a powerful strength, endurance, agility, and flexibility exercise as well as an excellent developer of the muscles of the legs.

Note: Do not start using this exercise until the second week of exercising.

Starting position:
Full squat position.

Exercise:
1. Jump high into the air spreading legs outward and upward keeping knees straight, touching toes to hands.

2. Let gravity take you to the starting position.

3. Repeat.

Dosage: 2-10 times.

Conditioning tips:

A boxer should never permit his legs to get out of condition. Vigorous walking or running should be a part of his daily routine.

Be sure to loosen the muscles of the legs and trunk before boxing.

Injuries to the bones of the hands and wrists may be avoided by using the hand in the proper position when striking an opponent and by increasing the strength of the wrists. Wrist strength is very important in boxing. Wrists can be strengthened by:

A. Climbing the regulation gym rope.

B. Grasping the rungs of the horizontal ladder and walking forward and backward.

C. Mounting the parallel bars and walking forward and backward while keeping the body in an erect position and knees straight throughout the exercise.

D. Rope skipping. (This activity also promotes endurance, and develops the foot and leg muscles.)

FOOTBALL

Most football coaches use conditioning exercises throughout the season. At the beginning of the season fifteen minutes may well be given to these exercises, while later on in the season five minutes may be sufficient.

The most important physical qualities for playing football are probably endurance, speed, agility, strength, power, and balance. The muscles of the arms, shoulders, back, and legs must be strong.

The following conditioning exercises are recommended for football for a period of three weeks:

Sit Ups

This exercise is excellent for strengthening the abdominal muscles. Try to pull abdomen well in throughout the exercise.

Starting position:
Lying on back with arms above head on the floor.

Exercise:
1. Sit up and touch toes. Keep legs straight. Exhale.
2. Roll back to floor, extending arms in line with body.
3. Repeat.

Dosage: 10-20 times.

Note: After two weeks do the "Sit Ups" as follows:

1. Clasp the hands behind the neck in the lying position.
2. Sit up and touch right elbow to left knee. Exhale.
3. Roll back to floor.
4. Sit up and touch left elbow to right knee. Exhale.
5. Roll back to floor.
6. Repeat.

Roll and Sit Through

This exercise tests your abdominal muscles. It also develops flexibility, agility, and skill in the use of your body. If you find difficulty in "sitting through" (movement number 6), you may solve this difficulty by reducing the size of your abdomen.

Starting position:

Lying on back with arms above head on the floor and legs straight.

Exercise:

1. Bring knees to chest, grasp hard with hands. Exhale.
2. Stretch legs straight, heels six inches off floor, hands above head in line with the body (not touching floor).
3. Roll either right or left keeping feet and hands free from floor.
4. Place hands on floor under chest.
5. Extend arms raising weight on hands and feet.
6. Sit through, bending knees sharply and sliding feet forward *between* hands. Exhale.
7. Assume starting position and repeat.

Dosage: 4-10 times.

Jumping Jack

This exercise strengthens the muscles of the thighs, calves, and feet. This is a fine test of endurance.

Starting position:

Standing, feet apart, arms over head.

Exercise:

1. Jump to squat, hands on hips. Exhale.
2. Spring back to original position. Inhale.
3. Repeat.

Dosage: 30 seconds to one minute.

The Pincer Movement

This exercise uses practically all the muscles of the body. For endurance, co-ordination, and flexibility. Especially recommended for strengthening abdominal muscles.

Starting position:

Lying on back, arms at side shoulder level.

Exercise:

1. Kick right foot to left hand and return. Exhale.
2. Kick left foot to right hand and return. Exhale.
3. Sit up, with legs spread wide apart. Exhale.
4. Swing right hand to left foot. Exhale.
5. Swing left hand to right foot. Exhale.
6. Roll to original position.
7. Repeat.

Dosage: 4-10 times.

Paddy Cake

This exercise develops the chest, shoulders, arms, and wrists. The extending of the legs to the rear as the weight is supported on the hands, and the returning of the feet to the squat position develops the abdominal muscles. Hold abdomen well in throughout this exercise. You are expected to breathe deeply throughout and following this exercise. Do not give up too quickly. Fitness only comes when you work your body somewhere near the limit of your endurance.

This exercise progresses through stages.

First stage

Starting position:
  Standing erect.

Exercise:
  1. Squat to full knee bend, hands outside of feet. Exhale.
  2. Extend legs to prone rest position.
  3. Jump back to position 1. Exhale.
  4. Spring to erect position.
  5. Repeat.

Dosage: 6-10 times.

Note: When 10 times becomes easy, or after one week of doing the exercise, do the second stage.

Second stage

Starting position:
  Hands on floor, arms extended, legs extended to prone rest position.

Exercise:
  1. Dip and touch chest (not knees or abdomen) to floor. Exhale.
  2. Extend arms to starting position.
  3. Repeat. (Keep the back straight.)

Dosage: 4-10 times.

Note: When 10 times becomes easy do the third stage.

Third stage

Starting position:

Standing erect.

Exercise:

1. Squat to full knee bend, hands outside of feet. Exhale.
2. Extend legs to prone rest position.
3. Dip and touch chest to floor. Exhale.
4. Extend arms, clap hands and catch weight on palms.
5. Jump to position 1. Exhale.
6. Spring to erect position.
7. Repeat.

Dosage: 6-12 times.

THE "V"

Victory over weak abdominal muscles! This exercise looks simple. Vigorous exercise of the abdominal and leg muscles. It also helps to improve balance.

Starting position:

Lying on back, hands on abdomen which is pulled in.

Exercise:

1. Raise legs six inches, throwing body in a sitting position as legs are spread wide apart, *heels off floor*.
2. Close legs. Exhale.

3. Lower trunk to lying position and lower heels to floor.
4. Repeat.

Dosage: 4-12 times.

HIT THE DECK

This exercise tests your endurance. The dive to the floor demands good hand, wrist, and arm strength and skill in the control of the body—and courage.

Starting position:
High-step run in place for 10 seconds.

Exercise:
1. Dive forward, weight on hands and let first the chest touch the floor *lightly,* then the abdomen, then the thighs, and feet. (Be sure to point toes.) Relax for 5 seconds.
2. Jump to feet.
3. Repeat.

Dosage: 4-10 times.

SINGLE TREADMILL

This exercise is a mild endurance exercise plus flexibility.

Starting position:
One-half dip position with right knee bent under chest, left leg extended back full length.

Exercise:

Rapidly change positions of feet by jumping motions. Be sure forward foot comes up between hands.

Dosage: 30 seconds or 15-30 changes.

DOUBLE TREADMILL

This exercise is a vigorous endurance exercise which gradually involves the hip and thigh muscles.

Starting position:

One-half dip position with both legs extended back full length.

Exercise:
1. Bring both knees up under chest with a jumping motion. Exhale.
2. Return feet to starting position with a rapid jumping motion.

Dosage: 15-30 seconds.

THE RUSSIAN

This exercise is a vigorous endurance exercise for the legs. Flexibility, agility, and balance are developed—but gradually. Avoid if you have a "trick" or weak knee.

Starting position:

Full squat, right leg straight forward with heel on floor.

Exercise:

1. Change leg position, placing left leg forward and right foot under body in full squat position. Exhale.
2. Repeat.

Dosage: 10-30 seconds or 6-20 changes.

JACK KNIFE

This exercise is a vigorous abdominal exercise and involves a high degree of balance, flexibility, and agility.

Starting position:

Lying on back, hands at sides.

Exercise:

1. Raise trunk and legs off floor keeping knees straight.
2. Touch toes with fingers. Exhale.
3. Return to starting position.
4. Repeat.

Dosage: 5-20 times.

THE JEEP

This exercise is a powerful strength, endurance, agility, and flexibility exercise as well as an excellent developer of the muscles of the legs.

Note: Do not start using this exercise until the second week of exercising.

Starting position:

Full squat position.

Exercise:

1. Jump high into the air spreading legs outward and upward keeping knees straight, touching toes to hands.
2. Let gravity take you to the starting position.
3. Repeat.

Dosage: 2-10 times.

FISH FLOP

This exercise is a vigorous abdominal exercise and a hip reducer as well.

Starting position:

Lying on back, hands clasped behind neck, knees on chest.

Exercise:

1. Twist and throw knees to right.
2. Twist and throw knees to left.
3. Repeat. (Each twist should be made quickly.)

Dosage: 4-16 times.

Other good football exercises:

DUCK WADDLE

Position—full squat, one arm resting on thigh, other hand touching ground.

Action—walk in this position 10 to 20 yards.

Note: Stay low in the full squat position. This exercise is excellent to condition the knees. The dosage may be increased to any distance.

GRASS DRILL. (This is very popular.)

Position—squad line up in rows with three yards between players. The following commands are given:

1. *Command*   2. *Action*

"Go"   Running in place.

"Down"   Dive to ground, hands and chest first.

"Right"   Throw the body on right side.

"Left"   Throw body on left side.

"Back"   Throw body on back.

"Up"   Lying on back, feet in air, bicycling.

These commands may be given in any order, and they should be changed quickly. The action will differ somewhat depending upon the previous position. For example, if a player is executing the "Go" command, "Right" would mean that he throw his body to the ground on his right side. However, if "Right" followed a position where the player is on the ground he would merely roll to his right side.

Note: In giving exercises to a football squad, best results can be secured if the coach will:

1. Put plenty of pep into each exercise.
2. Keep up an intermittent chatter of encouragement.
3. Repeat each exercise only a few times at first to avoid undue fatigue.
4. Change from one exercise to another without any pause.
5. Remember, in addition to muscular strength, emphasis must be given to timing and rhythm. Skilful movements must be the goal.

Conditioning tips:

Football coaching is a race against time. Players should be urged to report at the beginning of the season in the best possible physical condition. The season is short, and there is never sufficient time to accomplish all that needs to be done. Consequently, there is danger of over-working a team. Scrimmage is not a toughening process, but on the contrary, if excessively used it will soften a team. Remember, you want your team in top physical and mental condition the day of the game.

GYMNASTICS

Flexibility, strength, and balance are essential in gymnastics. The following conditioning exercises are recommended for the first three weeks of the season, in addition to rope climbing, chinning, and arm and leg work on the stall bars:

Roll and Sit Through

This exercise tests your abdominal muscles. It also develops flexibility, agility, and skill in the use of your body.

Starting position:
Lying on back with arms above head on the floor and legs straight.

Exercise:
1. Bring knees to chest, grasp hard with hands. Exhale.
2. Stretch legs straight, heels six inches off floor, hands above head in line with the body (not touching floor).
3. Roll either right or left keeping feet and hands free from floor.
4. Place hands on floor under chest.
5. Extend arms raising weight on hands and feet.
6. Sit through, bending knees sharply and sliding feet forward *between* hands. Exhale.
7. Assume starting position and repeat.

Dosage: 4-10 times.

The Pincer Movement

This exercise uses practically all the muscles of the body. For endurance, co-ordination, and flexibility. Especially recommended for strengthening abdominal muscles.

Starting position:

Lying on back, arms at side shoulder level.

Exercise:

1. Kick right foot to left hand and return. Exhale.
2. Kick left foot to right hand and return. Exhale.
3. Sit up, with legs spread wide apart. Exhale.
4. Swing right hand to left foot. Exhale.
5. Swing left hand to right foot. Exhale.
6. Roll to original position.
7. Repeat.

Dosage: 4-10 times.

PADDY CAKE

This exercise develops the chest, shoulders, arms, and wrists. The extending of the legs to the rear as the weight is supported on the hands, and the returning of the feet to th squat position develops the abdominal muscles. Hold abdomen well in throughout this exercise. You are expected to breathe deeply throughout and following this exercise. Do not give up too quickly. Fitness only comes when you work your body somewhere near the limit of your endurance.

This exercise progresses until the most difficult stage is reached.

First stage

Starting position:

Standing erect.

Exercise:

1. Squat to full knee bend, hands outside of feet. Exhale.
2. Extend legs to prone rest position.
3. Jump back to position 1. Exhale.

4. Spring to erect position.

5. Repeat.

Dosage: 6-10 times.

Note: When 10 times becomes easy, or after one week of doing the exercise, do the second stage.

Second stage

Starting position:

Hands on floor, arms extended, legs extended to prone rest position.

Exercise:

1. Dip and touch chest (not knees or abdomen) to floor. Exhale.

2. Extend arms to starting position.

3. Repeat. (Keep the back straight.)

Dosage: 4-10 times.

Note: When 10 times becomes easy do the third stage.

Third stage

Starting position:

Standing erect.

Exercise:

1. Squat to full knee bend, hands outside of feet. Exhale.

2. Extend legs to prone rest position.

3. Dip and touch chest to floor. Exhale.

4. Extend arms, clap hands and catch weight on palms.
5. Jump to position 1. Exhale.
6. Spring to erect position.
7. Repeat.

Dosage: 6-12 times.

The "V"

Victory over weak abdominal muscles! This exercise looks simple. Vigorous exercise of the abdominal and leg muscles. It also helps to improve balance.

Starting position:
Lying on back, hands on abdomen which is pulled in.

Exercise:
1. Raise legs six inches, throwing body in a sitting position as legs are spread wide apart, *heels off floor.*
2. Close legs. Exhale.
3. Lower trunk to lying position and lower heels to floor.
4. Repeat.

Dosage: 4-12 times.

Hit the Deck

This exercise tests your endurance. The dive to the floor demands good hand, wrist, and arm strength and skill in the control of the body—and courage.

Starting position:

High-step run in place for 10 seconds.

Exercise:

1. Dive forward, weight on hands and let first the chest touch the floor *lightly,* then the abdomen, then the thighs, and feet. (Be sure to point toes.) Relax for 5 seconds.
2. Jump to feet.
3. Repeat.

Dosage: 4-10 times.

BOTTOMS UP

This exercise stretches the hamstrings (tendons at the back surface of the knee joint). Loss of flexibility of tendons is a sign of "getting old!" Here is one way to stay young.

Starting position:

Squat position, fingers grasping toes.

Exercise:

1. Straighten knees, keeping feet flat on floor and maintaining grasp of toes. Exhale.
2. Return to starting position.
3. Repeat.

Dosage: 10-20 times.

SINGLE TREADMILL

This exercise is a mild endurance exercise plus flexibility.

Starting position:

One-half dip position with right knee bent under chest, left leg extended back full length.

Exercise:

Rapidly change positions of feet by jumping motions.

Dosage: 30 seconds or 15-30 changes.

THE RUSSIAN

This exercise is a vigorous endurance exercise for the legs. Flexibility, agility, and balance are developed—but gradually. Avoid if you have a "trick" or weak knee.

Starting position:

Full squat, right leg straight forward with heel on floor.

Exercise:

1. Change leg position, placing left leg forward and right foot under body in full squat position. Exhale.
2. Repeat.

Dosage: 10-30 seconds or 6-20 changes.

JACK KNIFE

This exercise is a vigorous abdominal exercise and involves a high degree of balance, flexibility, and agility.

Starting position:

Lying on back, hands at sides.

Exercise:

1. Raise trunk and legs off floor keeping knees straight.
2. Touch toes with fingers. Exhale.
3. Return to starting position.
4. Repeat.

Dosage: 5-20 times.

FISH FLOP

This exercise is a vigorous abdominal exercise and a hip reducer as well.

Starting position:

Lying on back, hands behind neck held firm, knees on chest.

Exercise:

1. Twist and throw knees to right.
2. Twist and throw knees to left.
3. Repeat. (Each twist should be made quickly.)

Dosage: 4-16 times.

Conditioning tips:

Practice for gymnastics is not drudgery, and a coach must guard against over-working his squad. After the squad is in good condition, practice during the week should be fairly light—work on routine—but do not work hard every day. Rest the squad the day before a meet.

It is very important to have the abdominal muscles well-developed for all gymnastic activities.

SWIMMING

Flexibility, strength, and endurance are necessary for swimming. To maintain good physical condition when the season is not in progress and especially before the season opens, the following exercises are recommended:

Sit Ups

This exercise is excellent for strengthening the abdominal muscles. Try to pull abdomen well in throughout the exercise.

Starting position:
Lying on back with arms above head on the floor.

Exercise:
1. Sit up and touch toes. Keep legs straight. Exhale.
2. Roll back to floor, extending arms in line with body.
3. Repeat.

Dosage: 10-20 times.

Note: After two weeks do the "Sit Ups" as follows:

1. Clasp the hands behind the neck in the lying position.
2. Sit up and touch right elbow to left knee. Exhale.
3. Roll back to floor.
4. Sit up and touch left elbow to right knee. Exhale.
5. Roll back to floor.
6. Repeat.

Jumping Jack

This exercise strengthens the muscles of the thighs, calves, and feet. This is a fine test of endurance.

Starting position:

Standing, feet apart, arms over head.

Exercise:

1. Jump to squat, hands on hips. Exhale.
2. Spring back to original position. Inhale.
3. Repeat.

Dosage: 30 seconds to one minute.

THE PINCER MOVEMENT

This exercise uses practically all the muscles of the body. For endurance, co-ordination, and flexibility. Especially recommended for strengthening abdominal muscles.

Starting position:

Lying on back, arms at side shoulder level.

Exercise:

1. Kick right foot to left hand and return. Exhale.
2. Kick left foot to right hand and return. Exhale.
3. Sit up, with legs spread wide apart. Exhale.
4. Swing right hand to left foot. Exhale.
5. Swing left hand to right foot. Exhale.
6. Roll to original position.
7. Repeat.

Dosage: 4-10 times.

THE DIPPER

Moderate exercise for arms, but especially beneficial for developing strength and flexibility of ankles and feet.

Starting position:
Prone leaning rest position, but with weight on upper portion of toes.

Exercise:
1. Lower chest to floor, exhale. Do not touch abdomen or knees to floor.
2. Return to original position.

Dosage: 6-10 times.

THE "V"

Victory over weak abdominal muscles! This exercise looks simple. Vigorous exercise of the abdominal and leg muscles. It also helps to improve balance.

Starting position:
Lying on back, hands on abdomen which is pulled in.

Exercise:
1. Raise legs six inches, throwing body in a sitting position as legs are spread wide apart, *heels off floor.*
2. Close legs. Exhale.
3. Lower trunk to lying position and lower heels to floor.
4. Repeat.

Dosage: 4-12 times.

Bottoms Up

This exercise stretches the hamstrings (tendons at the back surface of the knee joint). Loss of flexibility of tendons is a sign of "getting old!" Here is one way to stay young.

Starting position:

Squat position, fingers grasping toes.

Exercise:

1. Straighten knees, keeping feet flat on floor and maintaining grasp of toes. Exhale.
2. Return to starting position.
3. Repeat.

Dosage: 10-20 times.

Leg Lifter

This exercise stretches the muscles of the lower back and strengthens the muscles of the abdomen.

Starting position:

Lying on back, hands under head and elbows on floor.

Exercise:

1. With knees together and straight, extend legs upward to right angle to floor.
2. Keep elbows on floor, press heels toward ceiling six inches. (Legs are extended *up*.)

3. Return heels to a position six inches off floor.

4. Repeat.

Dosage: 4-16 times.

SINGLE TREADMILL

This exercise is a mild endurance exercise plus flexibility.

Starting position:

One-half dip position with right knee bent under chest, left leg extended back full length.

Exercise:

Rapidly change positions of feet by jumping motions.

Dosage: 30 seconds or 15-30 changes

FULL FLUTTER

Excellent conditioner for legs and arms of swimmers. Also, an ideal endurance exercise.

Starting position:

Lying prone, face down, arms and legs extended off floor.

Exercise:

Raise right arm and left leg. As right arm and left leg are lowered almost to floor, raise left arm and right leg. Repeat by rapidly alternating positions.

Dosage: 40-100 times.

JACK KNIFE

This exercise is a vigorous abdominal exercise and involves a high degree of balance, flexibility, and agility.

Starting position:

Lying on back, hands at sides.

Exercise:

1. Raise trunk and legs off floor keeping knees straight.
2. Touch toes with fingers. Exhale.
3. Return to starting position.
4. Repeat.

Dosage: 5-20 times.

Note:

For a complete coverage of conditioning during the season, as well as skills of swimming see the A. S. Barnes and Company 1942 publication, *"Swimming,"* by R. J. H. Kiphuth.

TRACK

Track demands all six of the fundamental qualities of fitness. Certain events, of course, require different qualities. Most track coaches believe in conditioning exercises for the entire squad. Due to the fact that track is an individual sport and the squad members usually do not all report for practice at a certain time, it is difficult to give conditioning exercises to the squad as a group. The exercises may be given in a group or each man on the squad may take them singly. If the latter procedure is followed, each man should be given exercises that condition best for his event. Track is recognized as being divided into field events and running events, but all body areas should be developed. The following exercises are recommended for track men for a period not to exceed three weeks:

Sit Ups

This exercise is excellent for strengthening the abdominal muscles. Try to pull abdomen well in throughout the exercise.

Starting position:
Lying on back with arms above head on the floor.

Exercise:
1. Sit up and touch toes. Keep legs straight. Exhale.
2. Roll back to floor, extending arms in line with body.
3. Repeat.

Dosage: 10-20 times.

Note: After two weeks do the "Sit Ups" as follows:

1. Clasp the hands behind the neck in the lying position.
2. Sit up and touch right elbow to left knee. Exhale.
3. Roll back to floor.
4. Sit up and touch left elbow to right knee. Exhale.
5. Roll back to floor.
6. Repeat.

Roll and Sit Through

This exercise tests your abdominal muscles. It also develops flexibility, agility, and skill in the use of your body.

Starting position:

Lying on back with arms above head on the floor and legs straight.

Exercise:

1. Bring knees to chest, grasp hard with hands. Exhale.
2. Stretch legs straight, heels six inches off floor, hands above head in line with the body (not touching floor).
3. Roll either right or left keeping feet and hands free from floor.
4. Place hands on floor under chest.
5. Extend arms raising weight on hands and feet.
6. Sit through, bending knees sharply and sliding feet forward *between* hands. Exhale.
7. Assume starting position and repeat.

Dosage: 4-10 times.

JUMPING JACK

This exercise strengthens the muscles of the thighs, calves, and feet. This is a fine test of endurance.

Starting position:

Standing, feet apart, arms over head.

Exercise:

1. Jump to squat, hands on hips. Exhale.
2. Spring back to original position. Inhale.
3. Repeat.

Dosage: 30 seconds to one minute.

The Pincer Movement

This exercise uses practically all the muscles of the body. For endurance, co-ordination, and flexibility. Especially recommended for strengthening abdominal muscles.

Starting position:
Lying on back, arms at side shoulder level.

Exercise:
1. Kick right foot to left hand and return. Exhale.
2. Kick left foot to right hand and return. Exhale.
3. Sit up, with legs spread wide apart. Exhale.
4. Swing right hand to left foot. Exhale.
5. Swing left hand to right foot. Exhale.
6. Roll to original position.
7. Repeat.

Dosage: 4-10 times.

Paddy Cake

This exercise develops the chest, shoulders, arms, and wrists. The extending of the legs to the rear as the weight is supported on the hands, and the returning of the feet to the squat position develops the abdominal muscles. Hold abdomen well in throughout this exercise. You are expected to breathe deeply throughout and following this exercise. Do not give up too quickly. Fitness only comes when you work your body somewhere near the limit of your endurance.

This exercise progresses until the most difficult stage is reached.

First stage

Starting position:
Standing erect.

Exercise:
1. Squat to full knee bend, hands outside of feet. Exhale.
2. Extend legs to prone rest position.
3. Jump back to position 1. Exhale.
4. Spring to erect position.
5. Repeat.

Dosage: 6-10 times.

Note: When 10 times becomes easy, or after one week of doing the exercise, do the second stage.

Second stage

Starting position:
Hands on floor, arms extended, legs extended to prone rest position.

Exercise:
1. Dip and touch chest (not knees or abdomen) to floor. Exhale.
2. Extend arms to starting position.
3. Repeat. (Keep the back straight.)

Dosage: 4-10 times.

Note: When 10 times becomes easy do the third stage.

Third stage

Starting position:
Standing erect.

Exercise:
1. Squat to full knee bend, hands outside of feet. Exhale.
2. Extend legs to prone rest position.
3. Dip and touch chest to floor. Exhale.
4. Extend arms, clap hands and catch weight on palms.
5. Jump to position 1. Exhale.
6. Spring to erect position.
7. Repeat.

Dosage: 6-12 times.

THE "V"

Victory over weak abdominal muscles! This exercise looks simple. Vigorous exercise of the abdominal and leg muscles. It also helps to improve balance.

Starting position:
Lying on back, hands on abdomen which is pulled in.

Exercise:
1. Raise legs six inches, throwing body in a sitting position as legs are spread wide apart, *heels off floor.*
2. Close legs. Exhale.
3. Lower trunk to lying position and lower heels to floor.
4. Repeat.

Dosage: 4-12 times.

Bottoms Up

This exercise stretches the hamstrings (tendons at the back surface of the knee joint). Loss of flexibility of tendons is a sign of "getting old!" Here is one way to stay young.

Starting position:
Squat position, fingers grasping toes.

Exercise:
1. Straighten knees, keeping feet flat on floor and maintaining grasp of toes. Exhale.
2. Return to starting position.
3. Repeat.

Dosage: 10-20 times.

Leg Lifter

This exercise stretches the muscles of the lower back and strengthens the muscles of the abdomen.

Starting position:
Lying on back, hands under head and elbows on floor.

Exercise:
1. With knees together and straight, extend legs upward to right angle to floor.
2. Keep elbows on floor, press heels toward ceiling six inches. (Legs are extended *up*.)

3. Return heels to a position six inches off floor.
4. Repeat.

Dosage: 4-16 times.

SINGLE TREADMILL

This exercise is a mild endurance exercise plus flexibility.

Starting position:
One-half dip position with right knee bent under chest, left leg extended back full length.

Exercise:
Rapidly change positions of feet by jumping motions.

Dosage: 30 seconds or 15-30 changes.

JACK KNIFE

This exercise is a vigorous abdominal exercise and involves a high degree of balance, flexibility, and agility.

Starting position:
Lying on back, hands at sides.

Exercise:
1. Raise trunk and legs off floor keeping knees straight.
2. Touch toes with fingers. Exhale.
3. Return to starting position.
4. Repeat.

Dosage: 5-20 times.

Fish Flop

This exercise is a vigorous abdominal exercise and a hip reducer as well.

Starting position:
Lying on back, hands behind neck held firm, knees on chest.

Exercise:
1. Twist and throw knees to right.
2. Twist and throw knees to left.
3. Repeat. (Each twist should be made quickly.)

Dosage: 4-16 times.

Conditioning tips:
Most track men do not work hard enough. In order to obtain maximum performance in track, each individual must push himself to the limit. Work hard but ease up two days before a meet.

Jumpers should stay off their feet as much possible the day of a meet.

WEIGHT LIFTING

Weight lifting requires a lot of strength and power. Balance is also important. The best conditioning is probably done by lifting the weights; however, the following exercises are recommended as a warm-up before actual lifting:

Sit Ups

This exercise is excellent for strengthening the abdominal muscles. Try to pull abdomen well in throughout the exercise.

Starting position:
Lying on back with arms above head on the floor.

Exercise:

1. Sit up and touch toes. Keep legs straight. Exhale.
2. Roll back to floor, extending arms in line with body.
3. Repeat.

Dosage: 10-20 times. \\, \2 , \3, \4

Note: After two weeks do the "Sit Ups" as follows:

1. Clasp the hands behind the neck in the lying position.
2. Sit up and touch right elbow to left knee. Exhale.
3. Roll back to floor.
4. Sit up and touch left elbow to right knee. Exhale.
5. Roll back to floor.
6. Repeat.

JUMPING JACK

This exercise strengthens the muscles of the thighs, calves, and feet. This is a fine test of endurance.

Starting position:

Standing, feet apart, arms over head.

Exercise:

1. Jump to squat, hands on hips. Exhale.
2. Spring back to original position. Inhale.
3. Repeat.

Dosage: 30 seconds to one minute.

THE PINCER MOVEMENT

This exercise uses practically all the muscles of the body. For endurance, co-ordination, and flexibility. Especially recommended for strengthening abdominal muscles.

Starting position:
Lying on back, arms at side shoulder level.

Exercise:
1. Kick right foot to left hand and return. Exhale.
2. Kick left foot to right hand and return. Exhale.
3. Sit up, with legs spread wide apart. Exhale.
4. Swing right hand to left foot. Exhale.
5. Swing left hand to right foot. Exhale.
6. Roll to original position.
7. Repeat.

Dosage: 4-10 times.

THE "V"

Victory over weak abdominal muscles! This exercise looks simple. Vigorous exercise of the abdominal and leg muscles. It also helps to improve balance.

Starting position:

Lying on back, hands on abdomen which is pulled in.

Exercise:

1. Raise legs six inches, throwing body in a sitting position as legs are spread wide apart, *heels off floor.*
2. Close legs. Exhale.
3. Lower trunk to lying position and lower heels to floor.
4. Repeat.

Dosage: 4-12 times.

BOTTOMS UP

This exercise stretches the hamstrings (tendons at the back surface of the knee joint). Loss of flexibility of tendons is a sign of "getting old!" Here is one way to stay young.

Starting position:

Squat position, fingers grasping toes.

Exercise:

1. Straighten knees, keeping feet flat on floor and maintaining grasp of toes. Exhale.
2. Return to starting position.
3. Repeat.

Dosage: 10-20 times.

LEG LIFTER

This exercise stretches the muscles of the lower back and strengthens the muscles of the abdomen.

Starting position:

Lying on back, hands under head and elbows on floor.

Exercise:

1. With knees together and straight, extend legs upward to right angle to floor.
2. Keep elbows on floor, press heels toward ceiling six inches. (Legs are extended *up*.)
3. Return heels to a position six inches off floor.
4. Repeat.

Dosage: 4-16 times.

CHIN UP

This exercise develops the muscles of the back. If possible have someone hold your feet for better leverage, or tuck your heels under a heavy davenport.

Starting position:

Lying prone, face down, hands at hips.

Exercise:

1. Raise trunk until chin is one foot from floor.
2. Return to starting position.
3. Repeat.

Dosage: 6-20 times.

Note: After two weeks vary this exercise as follows:

Starting position:

Lying prone, face down, hands clasped behind neck.

Exercise: Raise trunk and elbows until elbows are one foot from floor.

Dosage: 6-20 times.

The Russian

This exercise is a vigorous endurance exercise for the legs. Flexibility, agility, and balance are developed—but gradually. Avoid if you have a "trick" or weak knee.

Starting position:

Full squat, right leg straight forward with heel on floor.

Exercise:

1. Change leg position, placing left leg forward and right foot under body in full squat position. Exhale.
2. Repeat.

Dosage: 10-30 seconds or 6-20 changes.

Conditioning tips:

It would be wise for the beginner in this activity to use these exercises for two weeks before any actual work is done with the weights.

Take it easy. Development here should be slow and gradual.

WRESTLING

Strength, power, endurance, agility, and balance are important in wrestling. The following exercises are recommended:

Sit Ups

This exercise is excellent for strengthening the abdominal muscles. Try to pull abdomen well in throughout the exercise.

Starting position:

Lying on back with arms above head on the floor.

Exercise:

1. Sit up and touch toes. Keep legs straight. Exhale.
2. Roll back to floor, extending arms in line with body.
3. Repeat.

Dosage: 10-20 times.

Note: After two weeks do the "Sit Ups" as follows:

1. Clasp the hands behind the neck in the lying position.
2. Sit up and touch right elbow to left knee. Exhale.
3. Roll back to floor.
4. Sit up and touch left elbow to right knee. Exhale.
5. Roll back to floor.
6. Repeat.

ROLL AND SIT THROUGH

This exercise tests your abdominal muscles. It also develops flexibility, agility, and skill in the use of your body. If you find difficulty in "sitting through" (movement number 6), you may solve this difficulty by reducing the size of your abdomen.

Starting position:

Lying on back with arms above head on the floor and legs straight.

Exercise:

1. Bring knees to chest, grasp hard with hands. Exhale.
2. Stretch legs straight, heels six inches off floor, hands above head in line with the body (not touching floor).
3. Roll either right or left keeping feet and hands free from floor.
4. Place hands on floor under chest.
5. Extend arms raising weight on hands and feet.
6. Sit through, bending knees sharply and sliding feet forward *between* hands. Exhale.
7. Assume starting position and repeat.

Dosage: 4-10 times.

JUMPING JACK

This exercise strengthens the muscles of the thighs, calves, and feet. This is a fine test of endurance.

Starting position:
Standing, feet apart, arms over head.

Exercise:

1. Jump to squat, hands on hips. Exhale.
2. Spring back to original position. Inhale.
3. Repeat.

Dosage: 30 seconds to one minute.

PADDY CAKE

This exercise develops the chest, shoulders, arms, and wrists. The extending of the legs to the rear as the weight is supported on the hands, and the returning of the feet to the squat position develops the abdominal muscles. Hold abdomen well in throughout this exercise. You are expected to breathe deeply throughout and following this exercise. Do not give up too quickly. Fitness only comes when you work your body somewhere near the limit of your endurance.

This exercise progresses until the most difficult stage is reached.

First stage

Starting position:
   Standing erect.

Exercise:
   1. Squat to full knee bend, hands outside of feet. Exhale.
   2. Extend legs to prone rest position.
   3. Jump back to position 1. Exhale.
   4. Spring to erect position.
   5. Repeat.

Dosage: 6-10 times.

Note: When 10 times becomes easy, or after one week of doing the exercise, do the second stage.

Second stage

Starting position:
   Hands on floor, arms extended, legs extended to prone rest position.

Exercise:
   1. Dip and touch chest (not knees or abdomen) to floor. Exhale.
   2. Extend arms to starting position.
   3. Repeat. (Keep the back straight.)

Dosage: 4-10 times.

Note: When 10 times becomes easy do the third stage.

Third Stage

Starting position:

Standing erect.

Exercise:

1. Squat to full knee bend, hands outside of feet. Exhale.
2. Extend legs to prone rest position.
3. Dip and touch chest to floor. Exhale.
4. Extend arms, clasp hands and catch weight on palms.
5. Jump to position 1. Exhale.
6. Spring to erect position.
7. Repeat.

Dosage: 6-12 times.

THE "V"

Victory over weak abdominal muscles! This exercise looks simple. Vigorous exercise of the abdominal and leg muscles. It also helps to improve balance.

Starting position:

Lying on back, hands on abdomen which is pulled in.

Exercise:

1. Raise legs six inches, throwing body in a sitting position as legs are spread wide apart, *heels off floor.*
2. Close legs. Exhale.
3. Lower trunk to lying position and lower heels to floor.
4. Repeat.

Dosage: 4-12 times.

HIT THE DECK

This exercise tests your endurance. The dive to the floor demands good hand, wrist, and arm strength and skill in the control of the body—and courage.

Starting position:

High-step run in place for 10 seconds.

Exercise:

1. Dive forward, weight on hands and let first the chest touch the floor *lightly*, then the abdomen, then the thighs, and feet. (Be sure to point toes.) Relax for 5 seconds.
2. Jump to feet.
3. Repeat.

Dosage: 4-10 times.

LEG LIFTER

This exercise stretches the muscles of the lower back and strengthens the muscles of the abdomen.

Starting position:

Lying on back, hands under head and elbows on floor.

Exercise:

1. With knees together and straight, extend legs upward to right angle to floor.

2. Keep elbows on floor, press heels toward ceiling six inches. (Legs are extended *up*.)
3. Return heels to a position six inches off floor.
4. Repeat.

Dosage: 4-16 times.

DOUBLE TREADMILL

This exercise is a vigorous endurance exercise which gradually involves the hip and thigh muscles.

Starting position:
One-half dip position with both legs extended back full length.

Exercise:
1. Bring both knees up under chest with a jumping motion. Exhale.
2. Return feet to starting position with a jumping motion. Rapidly.

Dosage: 15-30 seconds.

CHIN UP

This exercise develops the muscles of the back. If possible have someone hold your feet for better leverage, or tuck your heels under a heavy davenport.

Starting position:
Lying prone, face down, hands at hips.

Exercise:

1. Raise trunk until chin is one foot from floor.
2. Return to starting position.
3. Repeat.

Dosage: 6-20 times.

Note: After two weeks vary this exercise as follows:

Starting position:

Lying prone, face down, hands clasped behind neck.

Exercise: Raise trunk and elbows until elbows are one foot from floor.

Dosage: 6-20 times.

THE RUSSIAN

This exercise is a vigorous endurance exercise for the legs. Flexibility, agility, and balance are developed—but gradually. Avoid if you have a "trick" or weak knee.

Starting position:

Full squat, right leg straight forward with heel on floor.

Exercise:

1. Change leg position, placing left leg forward and right foot under body in full squat position. Exhale.
2. Repeat.

Dosage: 10-30 seconds or 5-20 changes.

Jack Knife

This exercise is a vigorous abdominal exercise and involves a high degree of balance, flexibility, and agility.

Starting position:
Lying on back, hands at sides.

Exercise:
1. Raise trunk and legs off floor keeping knees straight.
2. Touch toes with fingers. Exhale.
3. Return to starting position.
4. Repeat.

Dosage: 5-20 times.

The Jeep

This exercise is a powerful strength, endurance, agility, and flexibility exercise as well as an excellent developer of the muscles of the legs.

Note: Do not start using this exercise until the second week of exercising.

Starting position:
Full squat position.

Exercise:
1. Jump high into the air spreading legs outward and upward keeping knees straight, touching toes to hands.

2. Let gravity take you to the starting position.
3. Repeat.

Dosage: 2-10 times.

Other recommended exercises are rope skipping, rope climbing, and bridging.

Bridging is excellent for developing the muscles of the neck, and it is also an essential wrestling skill.

Rope climbing and chinning develop arm and shoulder strength.

Rope skipping develops nimbleness on the feet.

Conditioning tips:

The beginning wrestler should not worry about wrestling too much.

The experienced man, who has the skills and techniques well mastered, should not wrestle to complete fatigue more than once a week.

The material in this chapter is the result of actual experience with athletic teams and conferences with outstanding coaches of the sports covered. Coaches differ in opinion as to what exercises will best condition their players. Use the suggested exercises until you find something that you like better. Remember that a well-conditioned athlete will perform better than a poorly conditioned one.

CHAPTER V

The Exercise Program for Men.

The optimum level of physical fitness should be the goal of everyone. However, the age of the individual must be considered before setting up a definite goal of fitness. Whether or not an individual has been exercising regularly must also be considered. While it is agreed that most Americans fail to push their bodies to the limits of their endurance, caution must be exercised as an individual grows older.

In general it may be said that men under 25 years of age should be able to perform all the exercises given in this chapter if they will refrain at first from doing them beyond the minimum number of times. By the end of the first week of daily exercise, each may be done one additional time until the maximum number of times for each exercise is reached. You are then ready for sports.

Men between the ages of 26 and 35 should be able to perform all the exercises excepting numbers 8, 14, and 16 the minimum number of times. This prescription should be followed for three weeks. At the end of the third week men in this age group should increase their exercise dosage by one additional time for each exercise until the maximum number of times for each is reached. When this goal has been reached the excepted exercises (8, 14, and 16) may be introduced and the entire series performed for three more weeks. You will then be ready for sports. But, remember your age!

Men between the ages of 36 and 45 should start by doing the following exercises the minimum number of times:

1—2—4—5—6 (first stage only)—7—9—10—11—13—17 and 19.

(See pages 85 through 98 for details.)

This prescription should be carried out for three weeks. At the end of this time each exercise may be done one additional time until the maximum number of times is reached for each exercise. When this point of fitness has been reached, the entire series of exercises, except 8, 14 and 16, should be started, doing each one the minimum number of times. After two weeks of this advanced program the dosage of exercise can be increased by doing each exercise one additional time until the maximum number of times for each exercise is reached. You will then be ready for sports. But, remember your age! If it is tennis, try doubles rather than singles.

Men 46 years and older should start by doing the following exercises the minimum number of times:

1—2—4—9—10—11—13—19—20 (See pages 85 through 98 for details.) This prescription should be followed for one month. The dosage of exercise can then be increased by doing each exercise one additional time until the maximum number of times is reached for each exercise. You will then be ready to take up the series as outlined for men between the ages of 36 and 45.

The following exercise series is offered as one means of achieving a high level of physical fitness. The ability to perform this series the maximum number of times indicates excellent physical fitness.

Note: It is very important that exercises be performed daily. Should circumstances make it impossible to do them any day, substitute vigorous walking. Make four miles or more your goal.

EXERCISE NO. 1 *

ATTACKING ALL "FRONTS"

This exercise is essential to develop good posture. The ability to draw in the abdomen and extend the muscles of the lower back is necessary if one is to maintain a satisfactory posture. In this position the pelvis acts as a support for the spinal column and the abdominal organs. With the body in poor posture the lower back is hollow and the abdomen protrudes forward. Exercise No. 1 attempts to remedy this poor posture position by placing the lower segment of the trunk in a position which will allow the chest segment to assume a correct position. With the two lower segments in proper position it is easier to keep the head properly aligned. This exercise is also excellent for conditioning the muscles of the

* From "Individual Exercises," by Stafford, De Cook and Picard, copyright, 1935, by A. S. Barnes and Co.

abdomen and lower back. The exercise may also be taken in an upright position.

Starting position:

Lying on back, knees bent, feet flat on floor, hands at sides.

Exercise:

1. Draw abdomen in, exhale as the back is forced to the floor by contraction of the buttocks and abdomen.
2. Relax, inhale, keep abdomen in and chest up.
3. Repeat.

Dosage: 10-20 times.

EXERCISE NO. 2 *

SIT UPS

This exercise is excellent for strengthening the abdominal muscles. Try to pull abdomen well in throughout the exercise.

Starting position:

Lying on back with arms above head on the floor.

Exercise:

1. Sit up and touch toes. Keep legs straight. Exhale.
2. Roll back to floor, extending arms in line with body.
3. Repeat.

Dosage: 10-20 times.

Note: After two weeks do the "Sit Ups" as follows:

1. Clasp the hands behind the neck in the lying position.
2. Sit up and touch right elbow to left knee. Exhale.

3. Roll back to floor.
4. Sit up and touch left elbow to right knee. Exhale.
5. Roll back to floor.
6. Repeat.

EXERCISE NO. 3

ROLL AND SIT THROUGH

This exercise tests your abdominal muscles. It also develops flexibility, agility, and skill in the use of your body. If you find difficulty in "sitting through" (movement number 6), you may solve this difficulty by reducing the size of your abdomen.

Starting position:
Lying on back with arms above head on the floor and legs straight.

Exercise:
1. Bring knees to chest, grasp hard with hands. Exhale.
2. Stretch legs straight, heels six inches off floor, hands above head in line with the body (not touching floor).
3. Roll either right or left keeping feet and hands free from floor.
4. Place hands on floor under chest.
5. Extend arms raising weight on hands and feet.
6. Sit through, bending knees sharply and sliding feet forward *between* hands. Exhale.
7. Assume starting position and repeat.

Dosage: 4-10 times.

EXERCISE NO. 4

JUMPING JACK

This exercise strengthens the muscles of the thighs, calves, and feet. This is a fine test of endurance.

Starting position:

Standing, feet apart, arms over head.

Exercise:

1. Jump to squat, hands on hips. Exhale.
2. Spring back to original position. Inhale.
3. Repeat.

Dosage: 30 seconds to one minute.

EXERCISE NO. 5

THE PINCER MOVEMENT

This exercise uses practically all the muscles of the body. For endurance, co-ordination, and flexibility. Especially recommended for strengthening abdominal muscles.

Starting position:

Lying on back, arms at side shoulder level.

Exercise:

1. Kick right foot to left hand and return. Exhale.
2. Kick left foot to right hand and return. Exhale.
3. Sit up, with legs spread wide apart. Exhale.
4. Swing right hand to left foot. Exhale.
5. Swing left hand to right foot. Exhale.
6. Roll to original position.
7. Repeat.

Dosage: 4-10 times.

EXERCISE NO. 6

PADDY CAKE

This exercise develops the chest, shoulders, arms, and wrists. The extending of the legs to the rear as the weight is supported on the hands, and the returning of the feet to the squat position develops the abdominal muscles. Hold abdomen well in throughout this exercise. You are expected to breathe deeply throughout and following this exercise. Do not give up too quickly. Fitness only comes when you work your body somewhere near the limit of your endurance.

This exercise progresses until the most difficult stage is reached.

First stage

Starting position:

Standing erect.

Exercise:

1. Squat to full knee bend, hands outside of feet. Exhale.
2. Extend legs to prone rest position.

3. Jump back to position 1. Exhale.
4. Spring to erect position.
5. Repeat.

Dosage: 6-10 times.

Note: When 10 times becomes easy, or after one week of doing the exercise, do the second stage.

Second stage

Starting position:

Hands on floor, arms extended, legs extended to prone rest position.

Exercise:

1. Dip and touch chest (not knees or abdomen) to floor. Exhale.
2. Extend arms to starting position.
3. Repeat. (Keep the back straight.)

Dosage: 4-10 times.

Note: When 10 times becomes easy do the third stage.

Third stage

Starting position:
Standing erect.

Exercise:

1. Squat to full knee bend, hands outside of feet. Exhale.
2. Extend legs to prone rest position.
3. Dip and touch chest to floor. Exhale.
4. Extend arms, clap hands and catch weight on palms.

5. Jump to position 1. Exhale.
6. Spring to erect position.
7. Repeat.

Dosage: 6-12 times.

EXERCISE NO. 7

THE "V"

Victory over weak abdominal muscles! This exercise looks simple. Vigorous exercise of the abdominal and leg muscles. It also helps to improve balance.

Starting position:

Lying on back, hands on abdomen which is pulled in.

Exercise:

1. Raise legs six inches, throwing body in a sitting position as legs are spread wide apart, *heels off floor.*
2. Close legs. Exhale.
3. Lower trunk to lying position and lower heels to floor.
4. Repeat.

Dosage: 4-12 times.

EXERCISE NO. 8

HIT THE DECK

This exercise tests your endurance. The dive to the floor demands good hand, wrist, and arm strength and skill in the control of the body—and courage.

Starting position:

High-step run in place for 10 seconds.

Exercise:

1. Dive forward, weight on hands and let first the chest touch the floor *lightly,* then the abdomen, then the thighs, and feet. (Be sure to point toes.) Relax for 5 seconds.
2. Jump to feet.
3. Repeat.

Dosage: 4-10 times.

EXERCISE NO. 9

BOTTOMS UP

This exercise stretches the hamstrings (tendons at the back surface of the knee joint). Loss of flexibility of tendons is a sign of "getting old!" Here is one way to stay young.

Starting position:
Squat position, fingers grasping toes.

Exercise:

1. Straighten knees, keeping feet flat on floor and maintaining grasp of toes. Exhale.
2. Return to starting position.
3. Repeat.

Dosage: 10-20 times.

EXERCISE NO. 10

LEG LIFTER

This exercise stretches the muscles of the lower back and strengthens the muscles of the abdomen.

Starting position:
Lying on back, hands under head and elbows on floor.

Exercise:
1. With knees together and straight, extend legs upward to right angle to floor.
2. Keep elbows on floor, press heels toward ceiling six inches. (Legs are extended *up*.)
3. Return heels to a position six inches off floor.
4. Repeat.

Dosage: 4-16 times.

EXERCISE NO. 11 *

SINGLE TREADMILL

This exercise is a mild endurance exercise plus flexibility.

Starting position:
One-half dip position with right knee bent under chest, left leg extended back full length.

Exercise:
Rapidly change positions of feet by jumping motions.

Dosage: 30 seconds or 15-30 changes.

EXERCISE NO. 12

DOUBLE TREADMILL

This exercise is a vigorous endurance exercise which gradually involves the hip and thigh muscles.

* From "Individual Exercises," by Stafford, De Cook and Picard, copyright, 1935, by A. S. Barnes and Co.

Starting position:
One-half dip position with both legs extended back full length.

Exercise:
1. Bring both knees up under chest with a jumping motion. Exhale.
2. Return feet to starting position with a jumping motion. Rapidly.

Dosage: 15-30 seconds.

EXERCISE NO. 13

CHIN UP

This exercise develops the muscles of the back. If possible have someone hold your feet for better leverage, or tuck your heels under a heavy davenport.

Starting position:
Lying prone, face down, hands at hips.

Exercise:
1. Raise trunk until chin is one foot from floor.
2. Return to starting position.
3. Repeat.

Dosage: 6-20 times.

Note: After two weeks vary this exercise as follows:

Starting position:
Lying prone, face down, hands clasped behind neck.

Exercise: Raise trunk and elbows until elbows are one foot from floor.

Dosage: 6-20 times.

EXERCISE NO. 14

THE RUSSIAN

This exercise is a vigorous endurance exercise for the legs. Flexibility, agility, and balance are developed—but gradually. Avoid if you have a "trick" or weak knee.

Starting position:

Full squat, right leg straight forward with heel on floor.

Exercise:

1. Change leg position, placing left leg forward and right foot under body in full squat position. Exhale.
2. Repeat.

Dosage: 10-30 seconds or 6-20 changes.

EXERCISE NO. 15

JACK KNIFE

This exercise is a vigorous abdominal exercise and involves a high degree of balance, flexibility, and agility.

Starting position:

Lying on back, hands at sides.

Exercise:

1. Raise trunk and legs off floor keeping knees straight.
2. Touch toes with fingers. Exhale.

3. Return to starting position.
4. Repeat.

Dosage: 5-20 times.

EXERCISE NO. 16

THE JEEP

This exercise is a powerful strength, endurance, agility, and flexibility exercise as well as an excellent developer of the muscles of the legs.

Note: Do not start using this exercise until the second week of exercising.

Starting position:
Full squat position.

Exercise:

1. Jump high into the air spreading legs outward and upward keeping knees straight, touching toes to hands.
2. Let gravity take you to the starting position.
3. Repeat.

Dosage: 2-10 times.

EXERCISE NO. 17 *

THE WORM

This exercise stretches the hamstring tendons and gives moderate exercise to the arms and legs.

* From "Individual Exercises," by Stafford, De Cook and Picard, copyright, 1935, by A. S. Barnes and Co.

Starting position:

Feet together and *parallel,* knees straight, body flexed at hips, back rounded so that hands touch floor in front of feet.

Exercise:

1. By a series of short steps with the hands, advance along the floor, keeping heels on the floor as long as possible until the body is straight and supported by the straightened arms and toes.
2. By short steps with the feet progress toward the hands. Steps should be four inches long.
3. Repeat.

Dosage: 30-200 feet.

EXERCISE NO. 18

FISH FLOP

This exercise is a vigorous abdominal exercise and a hip reducer as well.

Starting position:

Lying on back, hands behind neck held firm, knees on chest.

Exercise:

1. Twist and throw knees to right.
2. Twist and throw knees to left.
3. Repeat. (Each twist should be made quickly.)

Dosage: 4-16 times.

EXERCISE NO. 19

THE PISTON

This exercise is a vigorous abdominal exercise, and it also stretches the lower back muscles. Balance is needed in this exercise.

Starting position:

Sitting on floor, hands resting lightly on abdomen.

Exercise:

1. Bend left knee to the chest.
2. Extend left knee as the right knee is drawn to chest.
3. Continue alternating knees. Keep heels off floor.

Dosage: 10-50 knee bends.

EXERCISE NO. 20 *

THE HIP MASSAGE

This exercise involves all of the trunk, shoulder, and arm muscles. Strong abdominal muscles are the result of this movement.

Starting position:

Lying on back, arms extended at side shoulder level, palms up, legs extended in a vertical position.

Exercise:

1. With knees straight and together, lower both feet to right hand.
2. Raise feet to vertical position.
3. Lower feet to left hand, keeping knees straight and together.
4. Repeat.

Dosage: 2-16 times.

The Exercise Program for Women.

Exercise is a very important means of remedying the past neglect of the body. One should not give up hope even though the exercise program has been neglected in the past. Nature is very kind in that

* From "Individual Exercises," by Stafford, De Cook and Picard, copyright, 1935, by A. S. Barnes and Co.

forgiveness comes to those who are now willing to work to make amends for past neglect. The body quickly responds to exercise which is not too severe at the start.

Have you had your medical examination? Do not start your quest for physical fitness until you have had a medical examination! You are now ready to streamline your figure and awaken that sleeping beauty. Two important things must be agreed upon:

"I will eat less fattening foods, and
I will exercise regularly."

This is going to take a lot of self-discipline, but it will bring results and those spare hips, or reasonable facsimile of the same, will become less and less a part of you. Massaging the skin will not remove the underlying excess of fatty tissue, but eating less of the fattening foods and exercising regularly will. Yes, it may be a slow process, but reduction should be slow.

Certain body parts may not respond to exercise to the degree that you desire. Heavy breasts, for example, may be due to internal secretions or hormones from several endocrine glands, and neither exercise nor massage can control the variable states of these glandular tissues. Take your doctor's advice in these cases.

Now more than ever is the time to engage in recreative activities. Participation in sports such as horseback riding, golf, bowling, badminton, and tennis gives the participant that priceless sense of momentary detachment from the monotony of daily tasks. This ability to use sport activities during your leisure provides a type of wholesome recreation which raises your morale. It isn't a question of not having time. Your general health demands that you take time for healthful exercise!

The majority of "systems" of exercises for the ladies have two things in common: they emphasize an erect posture, and they stress the value of stretching the body. "Stretching, stretching from your toes to the top of your head will give the posture you desire." An aesthetic posture is impossible with inelastic, sagging muscles. Exercise is needed to strengthen your posture-supporting muscles. Good posture takes "years" off your appearance.

Many women succeed in reducing the waist, hip, and thigh girths by doing exercises of the "posture" type, although in many cases no actual loss of weight may result. If there is one place the average woman desires to be found lacking, it is on the scales. The more vigorous exercises can be recommended to tone up the sagging posture muscles and to remove weight as well.

For those who need to put on weight, exercise is helpful in stimulating the appetite. The overweight individual must naturally exercise harder and for a longer period than the person who is underweight. Remember the loss of the first ten pounds is the hardest task you have. Once you get the scales working backwards your task becomes less difficult. But, don't attempt to reduce more than two pounds a week.

The exercise program recommended "For the Ladies" is as follows:

ATTACKING ALL "FRONTS"

This exercise is essential to develop good posture. The ability to draw in the abdomen and extend the muscles of the lower back is necessary if one is to maintain a satisfactory posture. In this position the pelvis acts as a support for the spinal column and the abdominal organs. With the body in poor posture the lower back is hollow and the abdomen protrudes forward. Exercise No. 1 attempts to remedy this poor posture position by placing the lower segment of the trunk in a position which will allow the chest segment to assume a correct position. With the two lower segments in proper position it is easier to keep the head properly aligned. This exercise is also excellent for conditioning the muscles of the abdomen and lower back. The exercise may also be taken in an upright position.

Starting position:
Lying on back, knees bent, feet flat on floor, hands at sides.

Exercise:
1. Draw abdomen in, exhale as the back is forced to the floor by contraction of the buttocks and abdomen.
2. Relax, inhale, keep abdomen in and chest up.
3. Repeat.

Dosage: Minimum, 8; Maximum 16.

SIT UPS

This exercise is excellent for strengthening the abdominal muscles. Try to pull abdomen well in throughout the exercise.

Starting position:
Lying on back with arms above head on the floor.

Exercise:
1. Sit up and touch toes. Keep legs straight. Exhale.
2. Roll back to floor, extending arms in line with body.
3. Repeat.

Dosage: 6-10 times.

ABDOMINAL MASSAGE

This exercise develops your abdominal muscles. It also develops flexibility, agility, and skill in the use of your body.

Starting position:
Lying on back with arms above head on the floor and legs straight.

Exercise:
1. Bring knees to chest, grasp hard with hands. Exhale.
2. Stretch legs straight, heels six inches off floor, hands above head in line with the body (not touching floor).
3. Repeat.

Dosage: 4-12 times.

Jumping Jack

This exercise strengthens the muscles of the thighs, calves, and feet. This is a fine test of endurance.

Starting position:

Standing, feet apart, arms over head.

Exercise:

1. Jump to squat, hands on hips. Exhale.
2. Spring back to original position. Inhale.
3. Repeat.

Dosage: 8-16 times.

The Pincer Movement

This exercise uses practically all the muscles of the body. For endurance, co-ordination, and flexibility. Especially recommended for strengthening abdominal muscles.

Starting position:

Lying on back, arms at side shoulder level.

Exercise:

1. Kick right foot to left hand and return. Exhale.
2. Kick left foot to right hand and return. Exhale.
3. Sit up, with legs spread wide apart. Exhale.
4. Swing right hand to left foot. Exhale.
5. Swing left hand to right foot. Exhale.
6. Roll to original position.
7. Repeat.

Dosage: 2-6 times.

PADDY CAKE

This exercise tones up the muscles of the chest, shoulders, arms, and wrists. The extending of the legs to the rear as the weight is supported on the hands, and the returning of the feet to the squat position develops the abdominal muscles. Hold abdomen well in throughout this exercise. You are expected to breathe deeply throughout and following this exercise. Do not give up too quickly. Fitness only comes when you work your body somewhere near the limit of your endurance.

Starting position:
Standing erect.

Exercise:

1. Squat to full knee bend, hands outside of feet. Exhale.
2. Extend legs to prone rest position.
3. Jump back to position 1. Exhale.
4. Spring to erect position.
5. Repeat.

Dosage: 4-8 times.

Tendon Stretcher

This exercise stretches the hamstrings (tendons at the back surface of the knee joint). Loss of flexibility of tendons is a sign of "getting old!" Here is one way to stay young.

Starting position:
Squat position, fingers grasping toes.

Exercise:
1. Straighten knees, keeping feet flat on floor and maintaining grasp of toes. Exhale.
2. Return to starting position.
3. Repeat.

Dosage: 4-10 times.

Leg Lifter

This exercise stretches the muscles of the lower back and strengthens the muscles of the abdomen.

Starting position:
Lying on back, hands under head and elbows on floor.

Exercise:
1. With knees together and straight, extend right leg upward to right angle to floor.
2. Return right leg to floor.
3. Repeat using left leg.

Dosage: 20-40 times.

Single Treadmill

This exercise is a mild endurance exercise plus flexibility.

Starting position:
One-half dip position with right knee bent under chest, left leg extended back full length.

Exercise:
Rapidly change positions of feet by jumping motions.

Dosage: 15-30 seconds.

Chin Up

This exercise tones up the muscles of the back. It also helps to remove spare chins. If possible have someone hold your feet for better leverage, or tuck your heels under a heavy davenport.

Starting position:
Lying prone, face down, hands at hips.

Exercise:
1. Raise trunk until chin is one foot from floor.
2. Return to starting position.
3. Repeat.

Dosage: 4-10 times.

Note: After two weeks vary this exercise as follows:

Starting position:
Lying prone, face down, hands clasped behind neck.

Exercise: Raise trunk and elbows until elbows are one foot from floor.

Dosage: 4-10 times.

THE RUSSIAN

This exercise is a vigorous endurance exercise for the legs. Flexibility, agility, and balance are developed—but gradually. Avoid if you have a "trick" or weak knee.

Starting position:
Full squat, right leg straight forward with heel on floor.

Exercise:
1. Change leg position, placing left leg forward and right foot under body in full squat position. Exhale.
2. Repeat.

Dosage: 10-20 seconds or 4-10 times.

THE WORM

This exercise stretches the hamstring tendons and gives moderate exercise to the arms and legs.

Starting position:
Feet together and *parallel,* knees straight, body flexed at hips, back rounded so that hands touch floor in front of feet.

Exercise:
1. By a series of short steps with the hands, advance along the floor, keeping heels on the floor as long as possible until the

body is straight and supported by the straightened arms and toes.

2. By short steps with the feet progress toward the hands. Steps should be four inches long. (Keep feet pointed straight ahead.)
3. Repeat.

Dosage: 20-100 feet.

Fish Flop

This exercise is a vigorous abdominal exercise and a wonderful hip reducer as well.

Starting position:
Lying on back, hands behind neck held firm, knees on chest.

Exercise:
1. Twist and throw knees to right.
2. Twist and throw knees to left.
3. Repeat. (Each twist should be made quickly.)

Dosage: 4-10 times.

The Piston

This exercise is a vigorous abdominal exercise, and it also stretches the lower back muscles. Balance is needed in this exercise.

Starting position:
Sitting on floor, hands resting lightly on abdomen.

Exercise:

1. Bend left knee to the chest.
2. Extend left knee as the right knee is drawn to chest.
3. Continue alternating knees. Keep heels off floor.

Dosage: 10-30 times.

AND

Rolling is excellent for reducing the abdomen, thighs, and hips. Lie full length on the floor with arms and legs extended. Raise arms, head, and legs off the floor and roll. Make three or four complete rolls to the left and return. Keep the arms, hands, feet, and head off the floor throughout the exercise.

The above series should be done the minimum number of times for three weeks. At the end of this time increase the dosage by doing one more of each exercise daily until you are doing the entire series the maximum number of times. You are then ready to take up sports. Take lessons in golf, horse-back riding, swimming, or any other of the many activities which will provide you with that sense of detachment from the monotony of daily tasks. Recreation means re-creation.

In addition to these exercises, plan to try walking again. But walk correctly! Each step should be an exercise in grace, poise, and balance. Walk in a single straight line. The exercise "Attacking All Fronts" is very helpful in securing the correct body position for walking. Try this exercise while standing. With your head up, hold your ribs up off your hips, keep the abdomen in and your hips down, in, and under in back. Now, with your toes pointed straight ahead, take an easy, forward step and let your arms swing loosely. A test of fitness is your ability to walk four miles without undue fatigue or foot strain.

For physical fitness which will allow you to retain your feminine grace, eat a well-balanced diet, exercise regularly, and to make sure that you will maintain a high degree of fitness plan to walk *daily*. Start now and exercise every day. Make your goal sports and the wholesome recreation which they offer.

INDEX

Ages, exercises for different, 13, 84

Badminton, 99
Baseball, conditioning exercises for, 18-21
Basketball, conditioning exercises for, 21-28
Bowling, 99
Boxing, conditioning exercises for, 28-36

Conditioning:
    Drills (*see also Drills* for specific sports), 16
    Physical, 5, 6, 55
    Programs, 18, 21, 28, 37, 48, 55, 61, 69, 74, 85, 98, 100
    Tips, 20, 27, 36, 48, 55, 61, 69, 74, 83, 99

Drills (*see* Conditioning)
    Grass, 47

Endocrine glands, 99
Exercise:
    Abdominal, 18, 21, 24, 25, 29, 30, 31, 33, 40, 42, 62
    Arm, 36, 37, 40, 43
    Benefits of, 8
    Bridging, 83
    Chest, 40
    Endurance, 19, 20, 23, 25, 26, 27, 32
    Horizontal ladder, 36
    Leg, 20, 23, 26, 44
    Parallel bar, 37
    Posture, 80, 83, 85
    Program for men (*see* Conditioning Programs), 84
    Program for women, 98, 100
    Regularity of, 13
    Rolling, 47, 108
    Rope climbing, 36
    Rope skipping, 28
    Shoulders, 36, 37, 40
    Stretching, 21, 22, 32, 99
    Swimming, 60
    Warm up, 16, 20, 69
    Wrist, 36, 37, 40, 42, 43

Fatigue, physical, 9
Fitness:
    Mental, 1, 2
    Physical, 1, 2, 4, 6, 8
        Optimum level of, 84
    Road to physical, 7
    Social, 1
    Total, 2
Football, conditioning exercises for, 37-48

Golf, 99
Gymnastics, conditioning exercises for, 48-55

Health:
    Examination, 10, 14, 99
    Habits, 6
    Status, 2
Horseback riding, 99

Ladies, exercises for the, 14, 98-108
Lear, General, 3

Massage
    Abdominal, 101
    Hip, 46, 47, 98, 108
Metabolism, 14
Morale, 1, 99

Non-athlete, conditioning for, 12, 84, 98

Organization, 17
Overweight, 100

Philosophy, work-duty, 7
Physical Fitness (*see* Fitness)
    Fundamentals of, 15
Proficiency, motor, 1

Reduction, weight, 100

Self-sufficiency, feeling of, 9
Service, 4

109

Shirer, William, 2
Sports, conditioning for, 10, 15, 18, 21,
  28, 37, 48, 55, 61, 69, 74, 85, 98, 100
Swimming, conditioning exercises for, 55-
  61

Tennis, 85, 99
Time of day for exercise, 14
Time schedule for conditioning, 15
Track, conditioning exercises for, 11, 61-
  69

Underweight, 100

War, demands of, 5
Warm-up exercises, 16, 69
Weight lifting, conditioning exercises for,
  69-74
Wrestling, conditioning exercises for, 74-
  83
Wrist, prevention of injury of, 36, 37, 40,
  42, 43